THE
HUMAN BRAIN

THE
HUMAN BRAIN

By JOHN PFEIFFER

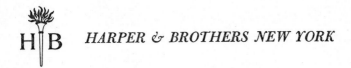 HARPER & BROTHERS NEW YORK

Library of Congress catalog card number: 54-12193

CONTENTS

ACKNOWLEDGMENTS

This book includes information gathered over a period of several years. It would have been impossible without the co-operation of brain investigators, psychiatrists and neurosurgeons who knew that what they had to say would be put into nontechnical English—for people without any formal training in science.

They gave most generously of their time in answering questions, and discussing patients and unpublished work. Just as important, they took extra time to check and criticize chapters based on their research findings. Any errors of fact or emphasis, however, are my own responsibility.

Special acknowledgment is due to Warren McCulloch of the Massachusetts Institute of Technology. He did not suggest this book, and might have regretted it if he had. But during conversations at his farm in Old Lyme and elsewhere, he made me aware of central problems in the study of the brain. His enthusiasm stimulated me, as it has many others. Also, a one-year grant from the Eugene F. Saxton Memorial Trust helped support an appreciable proportion of my research.

Many specialists have contributed to this book. The following is a partial list of those who were of particular help in interviews and correspondence: Gerhardt von Bonin, Ralph Gerard and L. J. Meduna of the University of Illinois College of Medicine; William German and Paul McLean of the Yale University School of Medicine; William Chapman and Robert Schwab of the Massachusetts General Hospital; K. S. Lashley, director of the Yerkes Laboratories of Primate Biology; Alfred Paul Bay, superintendent of the Manteno State Hospital; Pauline Cooke of Chicago; and Stephen L. Sherwood of the Middlesex Hospital in London.

Also, C. Judson Herrick of Grand Rapids, Michigan; Elizabeth C. Crosby of the University of Michigan Medical School; Ward C.

Halstead, R. W. Sperry, Heinrich Kluever and Robert E. Tschirgi of the University of Chicago; Mark Altschule and Jordi Folch of the McLean Hospital; Paul I. Yakovlev of the Harvard Medical School; Julian Bigelow and John von Neumann of the Institute for Advanced Study; Jay W. Forrester and Norbert Wiener of the Massachusetts Institute of Technology; Maurice W. Laufer, director of the Bradley Home; W. Grey Walter of the Burden Neurological Institute in Bristol, England; Ernest A. Spiegel of the Temple University School of Medicine; John C. Lilly of the National Institutes of Health; Claude Shannon of the Bell Telephone Laboratories; Antoine Remond of the National Center of Scientific Research in Paris; Clinton N. Woolsey of the University of Wisconsin Medical School; and Harold W. Magoun of the University of California School of Medicine.

THE
HUMAN BRAIN

1

INTRODUCING THE BRAIN

The human brain is three pounds of "messy substance shut in a dark warm place"—a pinkish-gray mass, moist and rubbery to the touch, about the size of a softball. Shock-absorbing fluid cushions it against bumps, sharp blows and other impacts. It is wrapped in three membranes, including an extra-tough outer envelope, and sets snugly in a crate of bone.

The brain is perched like a flower on the top of a slender stalk which in a six-foot man is not quite a yard long. The top three inches of the stalk, a thick white cable of nerve fibers known as the brainstem, lies entirely within the skull and is partly buried by the bulging halves or hemispheres of the brain. The rest of the long stalk, the spinal cord, is a direct continuation of the cable outside the skull. It runs down through holes in the vertebrae of the spine and ends at the small of the back.

Many branches extend from the central stalk, like the roads that feed traffic in and out of a superhighway. From the right side of the spinal cord thirty-one nerves pass through special windows between the vertebrae to the right side of the body. The same number of nerves pass by similar routes to the left side of the body. Besides the spinal nerves, there are a dozen pairs of cranial nerves which arise from the brainstem in the skull. Thus, eighty-six nerves connect the brain and the rest of the body. Through their finest fibers they reach into the remotest places, and into every nook and cranny

1

from the roots of hairs and teeth to the tips of the toes. This is the general structure of the nervous system.

The nervous system is made up of a large number of cells with long extensions or "tendrils." They come in assorted shapes—ovals, pyramids, bulbs, irregular blobs. The biggest have main bodies about two thousandths of an inch in diameter, and networks of fibers which may extend from a fraction of an inch to several feet. Under the microscope a single brain cell with its fibers may resemble the crown of a tree. Growing out from each branch are smaller branches, and from each of them comes a succession of smaller and smaller offshoots down to the most delicate twig. The brain contains some thirteen billion such cells, five times more than the total number of people in the world.

These units form masses of twisted fibers, a tangle which one investigator has called the "cerebral jungle." Until recently most investigators assumed that nerve fibers occupy fixed positions, or at least moved only as they grew, like the roots of plants. But new studies (at the University of Texas) indicate that brain tissue is far more active. As you read this sentence, fibers in your head are swaying like seaweed swept by tides. Tentacles of protoplasm are slowly moving forward, retreating, swelling and shrinking, waving from side to side.

Some twenty-three hundred years ago Hippocrates discussed this organ in terms which still make sense today: "And men ought to know that from nothing else but from the brain come joys, delights, laughter and sports, and sorrows, griefs, despondency and lamentations. And by the brain in a special manner we acquire wisdom and knowledge, and see and hear, and know what are foul and what are fair, what are bad and what are good, what are sweet and what unsavory. . . . By the brain we distinguish objects of relish and disrelish; and the same things do not always please us. And by the same organ we become mad and delirious, and fears and terrors assail us, some by night and some by day."

CONTROLS AND ADJUSTMENTS

What is the brain for? Judging by what we know today, it is the great organ of adjustment. It plays the basic biological role of keeping us adjusted to unpredictable events in the outside world, of preserving our identities in an environment of swift and ceaseless chemical change.

Parts of you are continually dying and being born again. Some three million of your red blood cells die every second. Or to look at it another way, three million red cells are born every second, because the body continuously calls up fresh reserves to keep the total count the same.

Similar processes take place throughout the body. Deposits of fat, which were once believed to serve as warehouses for storing food surpluses, are more like department stores during the Christmas rush. Your waistline may not change, but everything else does. Fat molecules are destroyed and replaced in a rapid round of biological activity. And the same thing goes for muscles, skin, tendons, blood vessels. Steady changes occur even in bones which seem to be the most inactive tissues of all. It has been estimated that every seven years or so the body negotiates a complete turnover of all its substance. In other words, your body does not contain a single one of the molecules that were "you" seven years ago.

These facts, many of them determined by modern methods of following radioactive tracers in the tissues, were not known to earlier biologists. They conceived of the body as a machine. Food was fuel, and the energy of combustion kept the machine going. All this took place within tissues that had to be repaired from time to time as they wore out. Otherwise they were relatively firm and unchanging structures. When the body was active, of course, it needed extra energy but during rest metabolism practically ceased until the next spurt of activity. We know that the actual situation is far different: all organisms must work merely to exist.

Life is more like a whirlpool than a machine. There is nothing machinelike about the vortex formed when water spirals downward. An entirely new whirlpool comes into being every few seconds as the rotating center replenishes itself from surrounding waters. But through it all the form does not change. The features of the vortex, the shape of the spinning funnel, remain the same over long periods of time. The system maintains its identity and structure—and your body is also a vortex of matter in a continual state of change.

Your brain keeps you alive by balancing the processes of birth and decay. These basic reactions have top priority. Everything else either helps in carrying them out, or else waits its turn. We pay a high price when the balance of any vital process is upset. For example, sugar is one of the body's energy-providing substances and we must have just the right amount, no more and no less. You are walking a biological tightrope between coma and convulsion, the possible results of relatively slight changes in blood sugar levels.

But the brain usually receives advance notice of impending trouble. It receives a steady flow of information about current sugar levels, and makes adjustments as effectively as a pilot guiding an airplane through a storm. If there is too much sugar, the excess is burned up and excreted. If there is too little, the liver is instructed to release the proper amount of reserve sugar. Notice what such control implies. The brain must "know" the desired sugar level, about a sixtieth of an ounce for every pint of blood, on the average. It must go by similar standards in regulating breathing (you probably inhale and exhale seventeen to twenty times a minute) and heart-beat rates (about seventy times a minute), and in holding body temperature at 98.6 degrees Fahrenheit.

The brain must also be in constant communication with all parts of the body. Indeed, it turns out to be the headquarters of the most elaborate communications network ever devised. Its activities are the result of the combined and patterned activities of billions of nerve cells. A nerve cell is a living wire which produces and conducts rapid electrical impulses. It keeps itself "loaded" and ready for action with the aid of a built-in battery which runs on an oxygen-sugar mixture and recharges automatically. It fires—that is, emits up to several hundred impulses a second—when triggering impulses reach it from sense organs or from other nerve cells.

These outside signals enter the body of the cell through special receiving fibers which are usually short, fine and highly branched. The cell also has a transmitting or "exit" fiber which, as a rule, is relatively long and thick. Its receiving fibers make delicate contact with the transmitting fibers of fifty other nerve cells on the average; some cells make contact with more than a thousand others. Thus signals are relayed from cell to cell as they pass through the nervous system. The rate at which a signal travels depends on the diameter of the fiber conducting it, the thickest fibers being high-speed express routes.

The slenderest fibers, about 1/25,000 of an inch in diameter, have speed limits of a foot a second or two thirds of a mile an hour. But in large-gauge fibers, which measure about ten times thicker, nerve impulses flash along at speeds up to 150 yards a second, a respectable 300 miles an hour. Thick fast fibers generally connect remote parts of the nervous system; thin slow fibers connect neighboring regions. Thus, if a cell communicates with several other cells at varying distances, the messages all tend to arrive at about the same time. This means that widely scattered parts of the nervous system can be stimulated, inhibited or alerted at once—a distinct advantage in co-ordinating complex behavior.

The brain uses this network to adjust us to the outside world. Generally speaking its operation can be divided into three parts: 1) it receives input in the form of messages from the sense organs; 2) it organizes the input on the basis of past experience, current events and future plans; and 3) it selects and produces an appropriate output, an action or series of actions. In the following sections we will discuss input and output, leaving the matter of what happens in between for later discussions.

STREAMS OF SENSATION

The brain keeps in constant touch with the flow of events. It is stirred up by lights, sounds, odors and other disturbances in the environment. Each sensation produces electrical impulses in nerves leading to the brain, "shocks" which stream into higher nerve centers and cause cell after cell to fire in a series of chain reactions. The nervous system includes one-way "sensory" channels, fibers carrying nothing but messages from sense organs.

The sense organs most remote from your brain are those located in your toes. Fibers originating in these outlying stations carry messages concerning heat, cold, muscle tension, touch, pain. They are joined by more and more fibers from your foot, leg, knee and thigh.

By the time the collected fibers reach the lower part of the spinal cord they form a thick cable. The cable continues to thicken as it climbs and is joined by millions of fibers from other organs of the body on the way up to the brain. This is the great ascending, sensory part of the nervous system. It subjects the brain to constant proddings. Although its lines are less busy during sleep, even then it is occupied with various duties—keeping your heart and lungs going, dreaming, and listening with a somewhat reduced vigilance. The brain relaxes but as long as it is alive, it finds no rest.

The brain's informers are sense organs, sentinels located at strategic points throughout the body. Imbedded in the skin are some 3,000,000 to 4,000,000 structures sensitive to pain, 500,000 touch or pressure detectors, more than 200,000 temperature detectors. These tiny organs—plus the ears, eyes, nose and tongue—are some of your windows to the outside world. Reports about the state of things inside your body come from other built-in sense organs which give rise to sensations of muscular tension, hunger, thirst, nausea. The number of senses is not known exactly. It is certainly more than five, and probably somewhere around twenty.

Each sense has its own fibers which carry its messages exclusively. But the fibers run together in the great ascending cable of sensory messages, and they are sorted and separated into smaller bundles in the brain. Each bundle ends in a different region of the cortex, the brain's outer layer or bark. This gray sheet of cells is the highest center of the nervous system, in two ways. It occupies top position, overspreading the brain like the dome of a cathedral, and it carries out some of the most advanced mental processes.

If the folded and crumpled cortex were spread out flat, it would cover more than two square feet (an area almost as large as the front page of your newspaper). Part of this area is reserved for maps of a special sort. For example, when a person listens to music nerve impulses representing the notes are flashed to a horizontal strip of cortex at the side of his head. Now imagine that the strip is exposed as he listens. Fine wires are placed at many points along the surface

The BRAIN

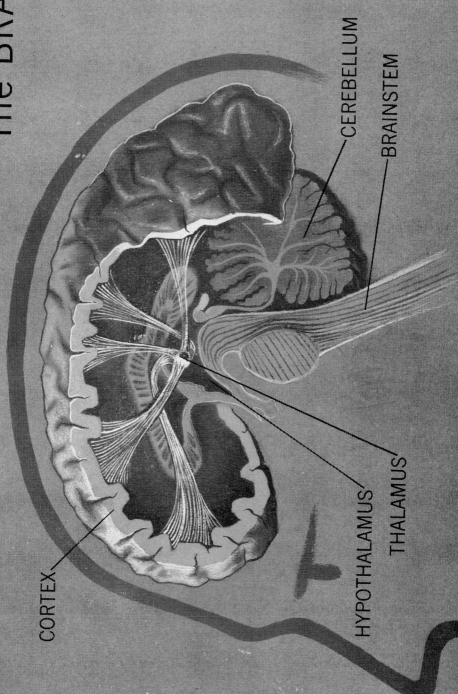

CEREBELLUM

BRAINSTEM

CORTEX

HYPOTHALAMUS

THALAMUS

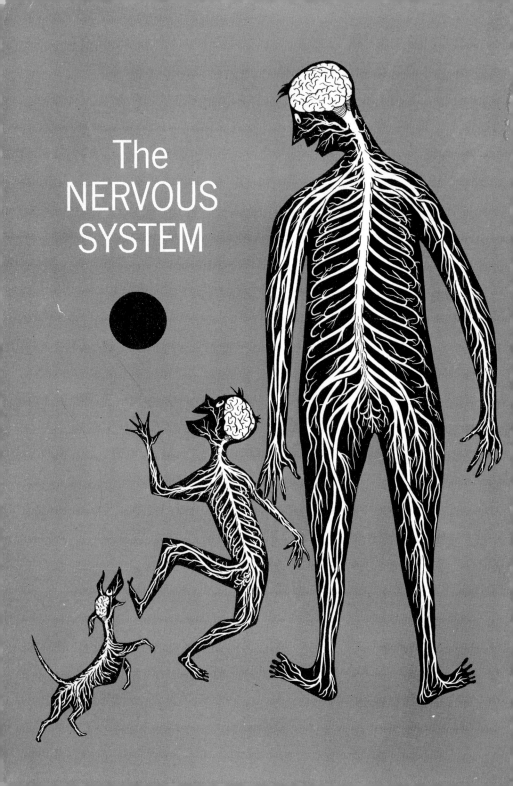

The
NERVOUS
SYSTEM

and attached to electronic recording equipment. Electrical signals representing different notes arrive at the strip and set up currents in the wires located there. These currents are detected and charted.

Roughly similar experiments have been performed on surgical patients and laboratory animals. The findings reveal that the strip at the side of your head is a kind of natural keyboard. The highest notes you can hear come in at the back end of the strip. The lowest notes come in at the front end. In between, the entire range of notes is represented by a sequence of precisely placed points. The octaves are marked off at regular intervals of about a tenth of an inch from the back to the front of the strip, that is, from high to low notes. Actually, of course, there are two strips—one on each side of the head, for the right and left ears.

Every note you hear has its sites on these strips and sends electrical pulses there. And, conversely, if the sites were stimulated artificially —say, by touching them with electrical probes—you would hear that note clearly, even though there was complete silence in the outside world. Theoretically, this offers the possibility of a new kind of subjective music played without instruments of any sort. You simply stimulate the proper points on the "hearing maps" of a person's cortex in the proper order. This doesn't mean that you would have to touch the surface of his brain with a probe. The trick might be done by remote control, with radio waves. In any case, by playing on the cerebral piano you could entertain him with classical music or perhaps a modern symphony composed especially for direct high-fidelity transmission to the cortex.

There is also an area which maps general skin sensations in fine detail. When you stub your right big toe or use it to test the water before you go in swimming, signals travel to the upper end of a strip of cortex running down the left side of your head. Sensations in your left big toe send signals to a corresponding part of a similar strip of the right cortex. Touch your ankles and messages flash to areas just below the toe areas on the strips. Leg signals arrive just below the ankle areas and so on down the sides of the cortex, from hips to fingers and from eyes to throat. Together the two strips form a map of the entire skin surface. Again, as in the case of sound, stimulating a point on this brain map produces a definite sensation —usually, a numbness or tingling—at a point on the skin.

The brain has other sensory maps. On the cortex at the back of the head are visual maps, screens made up of a mosaic of nerve cells. Every pattern you see around you, every tree and building and face, produces patterns on these screens as various cells in the mosaic fire. Other sensory fibers lead to the smell areas of the cortex, which are buried deep down in the walls of the chasm between the cerebral hemispheres. Each sense thus has its map on the cortex, its exclusive zone in the highest center of the nervous system. In this way, the brain sorts the information upon which its activities are based.

In nerve messages, as in dot-dash telegraph codes, patterns of pulses stand for the items of information being sent. But the interpretation of nerve signals depends first of all on the place they arrive at. No matter how accurately senses have been coded, no matter how meaningful the signals are, they will be misinterpreted if they arrive at the wrong place. A happy-birthday telegram means just that, even if it should happen to reach the wrong person. But a slip-up in the nervous system is something else again.

Supposing you were listening to fast music—say, the Benny Goodman version of "Sing, Sing, Sing"—and the nerve signals somehow got switched to the wrong line, arriving at the visual areas of the cortex instead of the hearing areas. You'd "see" the music as a mad rush of flashing lights, moving forms, vivid colors. Such mix-ups actually occur, and may result from "crosstalk" between nerve fibers. Crosstalk is familiar to repair men of your local telephone company. If insulation wears off neighboring wires in a telephone cable, electricity leaks away and you may find yourself listening in on someone else's conversation.

Similar leaks in the nervous system may account for many peculiar sensory disorders. Current escaping from a touch fiber to a nearby sound fiber, for example, might make you hear crashing noises when you bumped your elbow. Somehow certain drugs increase crosstalk among sensory fibers, and nerve injuries may produce the same effect. There is no reason to doubt that a certain amount of crosstalk takes place in the normal nervous system, the nerve signals traveling through neighboring fibers interact in some way. We do not yet know the significance of this effect. But new evidence indicates that crosstalk between fibers of the right and left eyes have something to do with the mechanism whereby we see objects as three-dimensional solids.

NERVES, MUSCLES, ACTION

For all its maps, however, the cortex is a good deal more than an atlas. Most of its cells belong to unmapped association areas, where different kinds of sensory information are brought together and related. Fresh sensory evidence from many maps is pooled and compared with remembered evidence. We feel emotions and conceive abstract ideas. As already mentioned, later chapters will present some theories about what happens in the association areas and how they are involved in surgery for mental illness. The following paragraphs deal with the net effects of these processes in directing certain forms of everyday behavior.

In tracing fibers upward from toes to brain, we have been considering only that part of the nerve network concerned with meaningful messages—sensory information arriving from the body and the outside world. It is also the origin, the point of departure, for outgoing messages addressed to muscles throughout the body. Since the messages cause us to move about, the fibers that carry them are called "motor" fibers and they make up the "motor" part of the nervous system. In other words, the brain serves as headquarters for descending motor as well as ascending sensory messages.

Sensory signals flow steadily into the brain; motor signals flow out. Sooner or later—and usually sooner—we go into action. All the centers of the brain exist to help us act more efficiently. Whatever the brain does, whatever problems it must solve, its decisions and conclusions and orders become impulses in the great system of descending motor nerves. These nerves carry messages from the cortex and brainstem and make contact with large motor nerve cells in the spinal cord, completing the last relays of the descending pathways. The pathways lead to muscle tissue. Each motor cell has a signal-transmitting extension which divides into tiny branches, each branch ending on a separate muscle fiber. The average motor nerve cell controls more than a hundred muscle fibers.

Action involves a shift from brain to brawn, from one type of remarkable tissue to another. We rarely put our muscles to the test, except perhaps in the heat of athletic competition or during emergencies. Several summers ago part of the grandstand collapsed during a baseball game in a small Pennsylvania town. A ticket-taker rushed to the scene, saw a young boy pinned under the wreckage, and lifted a large beam so that the child's body could be pulled to safety. The ticket-taker, an average-sized man in his late fifties, had lifted a total weight of more than five hundred pounds. Professional strong men have trained themselves to lift one thousand to fourteen hundred pounds, the weight of two concert-type grand pianos.

Muscles are composed of fibers that pull together in teams. The biceps in your arm contain 600,000 fibers too slender to be seen with the naked eye. Each fiber is a kind of cable made up of thousands of still smaller strands called fibrils. Magnified enormously under the electron microscope, the structure of each fibril appears as a series of fine dark bands, one above the other like the rungs of a ladder. Further study reveals that each fibril, in turn, consists of interlocked filaments—long-chain molecules less than two millionths of an inch wide.

These ultimate units of muscle are designed to do work, and a single fiber can lift a thousand times its own weight. We speak of muscles of steel, but the comparison fails to do justice to the real thing. Actually, your muscles are more like jelly. They are made up of protoplasm, a slushy semi-fluid which is three-quarters water. When you are relaxing, fibers and fibrils and filaments form a soft limp mass. The instant you start working, however, they contract and are transformed into a thick, tough elastic substance. Moreover, they can change from jelly to gluey plastic and back again hundreds of times a minute.

The entire nervous system participates, to some degree or other, in the control and co-ordination of these living fibers. They are always prepared for action. Motor nerve cells in the spinal cord discharge and charge five to ten times a second. This is their idling rate. Enough impulses stream to the muscles to keep them in proper states of tension. They are ready to stretch further or relax at an instant's notice from higher centers. As a matter of fact, certain muscles are continually relaxing and stretching. The brain is continually adjusting and readjusting the tensions of many muscles so that you maintain your posture and balance.

Simply standing up represents an acrobatic feat which is no less remarkable because it is performed automatically. Everyone naturally sways a bit in an upright position, and a failure in balance-controlling centers of the brain would send you sprawling. There is one powerful muscle which, if uncontrolled, would snap your leg back at the knee pressing your calf hard against your thigh. Another muscle would keep your leg stiff as a ramrod. The brain receives messages specifying the tensions of more than two hundred pairs of opposing muscles, every one of which must be properly adjusted to keep you standing.

Things become more complicated during a walk over uneven ground—and even more complicated when you dive from a high board, lower a sail in a storm or ride a surfboard. Every action, however simple, is made up of many individual muscle contractions and large-scale movements. These movements must follow one another at just the right time and in just the right order. The brain does the timing. It co-ordinates all sequences of movements so that we move smoothly and not in a series of jerks. When it comes to pursuing the activities of everyday life, we are thus reasonably sure of ourselves and our positions in the world.

Action involves other centers besides those which smooth our movements and control posture and balance. When you decide to move your foot, the decision is a nerve signal that comes from a particular region of the cortex known as the motor area. This strip of tissue is another map, and runs parallel and next to the strip for general sensation. Different parts of the body have their special sections on the map. The most active, not the biggest, parts rate the largest sections. If regular maps were similarly designed, they would look quite different from the familiar variety. In New York

City, for example, Central Park is many times larger than Times Square. But busy Times Square would be a huge section on an "activity" map, while the less hectic park would occupy a much smaller area.

On the motor-cortex map the trunk of your body and shoulders requires relatively little territory. But talking is such a frequent activity that your tongue and lips are considerably bigger than your back, as far as their areas on the motor strip are concerned. Your hands have the largest territory of all. As the most active parts of the entire body they need extra brain space, and provide a striking example of the close interworkings of nerve and muscle. To adjust the positions of the fingers and hands in space—which also means adjusting wrist, arm and shoulder—the brain controls thirty different joints and more than fifty muscles, for each hand.

In a fight your hands can be used as crude but effective weapons. Under less violent circumstances these same bludgeons are transformed into gripping and turning devices, and we can vary the power of our motions over a wide range. For example, opening the door of your car may take four hundred times more torque, or turning force, than working your telephone dial. It requires a force of only a fraction of an ounce to pick up a paper clip, while pulling on your socks and shoes calls for eight to twelve pounds. But if the need arises you can apply a right-hand squeeze of more than 150 pounds.

The hand, working under the direction of the brain, is capable of an unlimited variety of skilled manipulations. A master pianist can play 120 notes a second, or a dozen notes a second with each finger. One famous surgeon used to put a piece of silk thread in a matchbox and impress reporters with the following trick. Working within the cramped space of the half-closed matchbox, he nonchalantly tied the thread into complicated surgical knots—using only the thumb, index and middle fingers of his left hand. I once saw Dr. Dwight Harken of Boston make a series of tiny slip-knot stitches in a heart beating so violently that sewing seemed impossible. Yet the job took less than half a minute.

Every set of co-ordinated movements, from such highly skilled performances to routines like walking and driving a car, involve the integrating powers of the nervous system. All activities—direct or indirect, successful or unsuccessful—are attempts to keep the fires of life burning steadily and as long as possible. And this includes all our attempts to understand life itself.

From a biological standpoint, life is a complicated balancing act with no intermissions. Every second, billions of molecules in your body are being broken down and rebuilt. The forces of destruction and creation are equally necessary; the problem is to preserve the equilibrium between them. The interplay of the forces produces our tensions and strivings.

We have presented some basic facts about the brain and outlined the flow of events from sensory nerve impulse to muscle contraction, from sensation to action. Since the brain is the hero of this book, we have naturally emphasized its functions and the importance of the role it plays. Perhaps we should also emphasize that it is by no means an independent organ. It depends on the rest of the body when adjustments are called for—which is always. Our adjustments are never perfect. Things are too complex and too uncertain for that. Still, we do not and cannot stop trying, and the brain co-ordinates our continuing efforts.

2

MAN'S EVOLVING BRAIN

CONSIDERING the brain's pedigree, it is no wonder that we sometimes behave strangely. The surprising thing is that we spend such a large proportion of our lives behaving like human beings. The brain is a kind of menagerie. In a sense, it is a collection of nerve centers inherited from animals that lived in times past. You behave as you do because of tissues developed during more than a billion years of evolution. Like the fossil-bearing rocks of the earth, the most recent layers of the brain lie at the surface and ancient structures are piled underneath, one on top of the other.

Many species find a place in this strange totem pole. The forerunner of the spinal cord was an elastic rod. It formed in primeval worms, possibly a slimy crawler that pulled itself through the mud with the aid of a claw-shaped nose. Passing upward from the head end of the spine is like running through a high-speed motion picture of evolution. The levels are stages in the long history of the brain. They include, in ascending order, nerve centers which first appeared in fish, large creatures which resembled salamanders and could live in land or water, reptiles and mammals.

Spinal centers can take care of simple reflexes, such as pulling a burned finger away from a hot stove. More complicated actions are co-ordinated in the brain itself. The lowest section of the brainstem, the so-called medulla or bulb, helps regulate breathing and heartbeat rates, swallowing and other vital reflexes. You maintain your posture and balance with the aid of the cerebellum or "little brain," which lies one level higher and looks something like a ball of yarn. Attached to the brainstem at the back of the head, it offers a natural target for illegal rabbit punches in boxing.

The synthesis and breakdown of body chemicals involves the hypothalamus or "subchamber" at the upper end of the brainstem, about two inches back from the bridge of your nose. Still higher is the thalamus (chamber), a pair of bodies about the size of Brazil nuts which serves as the main relay station, the sorting center for sensory nerve fibers ascending to the highest centers. The activities we learn to perform automatically—walking, eating, shifting gears, starting a fast double play—are co-ordinated in a group of gray nerve bodies known collectively as the basal ganglia or "nerve masses at the base." At the very top of the pile is the most recently evolved center, the cortex.

This ensemble of nerve centers is the most complex organ ever created, at least as far as we know. It was shaped by countless evolutionary changes, modifications and revisions many of which have been discarded—and none of which was particularly spectacular or radical. But the cumulative effect of the individual steps has been enormous. It is the difference between an amoeba and a man. Nature accomplishes such results over vast stretches of time, the way she wears mountains away at the rate of a fraction of an inch every thousand years or so.

Like all organs, the brain is a product of a long series of small and unpredictable changes. These changes involve the mechanism by which living things pass hereditary traits from generation to generation. The color of your eyes and skin, the shape of your head, the quality of your brain—everything you inherit and pass on to your children—are transmitted by genes, protein molecules about five millionths of an inch long. Genes can be regarded as biological architects which see to it that the body is built according to hereditary blueprints.

A fertilized human egg contains some thirty thousand genes, each parent contributing about half the total. But the original genes must be copied and recopied many times over. The single egg cell becomes a newborn baby, a thing of many cells every one of which contains a complete set of genes. (Only sperm and egg cells each contain less than the full quota. They have half a share for the next generation. Half your child's heredity comes from you and half from your wife or husband.) In other words, genes are self-duplicating molecules. They reproduce, usually manufacturing exact images of themselves. Genes play a similar role in the heredity of all organisms.

But the image-making process doesn't always work perfectly. Sometimes a gene produces a molecule that differs slightly from itself, perhaps by the positions of only a few atoms out of millions. Such changes or "mutations," taking place over the ages in many species, are a major factor in determining the course of evolution. This is simply another way of saying that evolution is partly the result of imperfections, flaws in the self-duplicating processes of genes.

Geological changes may also be important. For example, supposing a population of fur-bearing animals is living in a moderate climate. Some of the animals, a very small proportion, happen to have extra-thick coats of fur. These "freaks" are the results of mutations, inherited genes that failed to produce exact images of themselves. Their extra fur is no help. In fact it may be somewhat stuffy, something like wearing a heavy coat in summer. But when an ice age comes—and no known fur-bearing animal can forecast the approach of glaciers—the eccentrics have an edge on their "normal" brethren. Similar mutations among the genes that form the brain and nervous system may lead to faster reflexes, more acute vision and other changes that increase an animal's general ability to cope with the world.

This is a rough outline of how species have evolved, that is, the random or chance part of the story. Notice that no plan or purpose is evident here. The changes in both genes and climate were accidents and it was sheer luck that they happened to work out together in the case of the fur-bearers. Many types of freaks find no advantages in their peculiarities. Mutations are rarely helpful. But given a particular heredity and environment, things tend to follow a natural logic of their own.

Whether a species survives or vanishes depends on biological laws as well as random events. As a leading investigator puts it, evolution is "an odd blend of the directed and the random, the systematic and the unsystematic." The following sections of this chapter present some facts and theories about the evolution of the human brain—the highest center or cortex first, and lower and more ancient centers later. We are still evolving along lines that can only be guessed at, and some of the guesses will be indicated.

The New Brain

The cortex, with its maps and association areas, is one of the most intensively studied tissues in biology. I have a 630-page book which is devoted entirely to a few square inches of the center, the motor strip described in the previous chapter. Many brain investigators believe that the cortex is the most human part of the human brain, and they have powerful arguments to back their point. For one thing, scientists are as much impressed with new things as the rest of us and the cortex is one of the latest additions to the brain. Geologically speaking, it was born yesterday, about a hundred million years ago.

The cortex began coming into its own when North America was a tropical cape jutting off the northeast part of Asia. Florida and the West Indies were still in one piece. The Rockies, thrust upward by tremendous pressures in the earth, had formed a natural dam against the Pacific Ocean. The result was a shallow inland sea that at one time or another spread from Arctic regions to the Gulf of Mexico and from Utah to the Mississippi River (Great Salt Lake is the last trace of this ancient sea). Animals which were to become human beings scurried about near steaming Montana swamps, but you scarcely would have noticed them.

Giant reptiles dominated the land—Tyrannosaurus with dagger-like teeth up to half a foot long, Brontosaurus big as a barn and weighing seventy-five tons. They moved awkwardly, butting through the jungles and pivoting with all the ease and grace of a moving van in a traffic jam. Their brains were small but quite adequate.

There was a crude cortex, but it held a relatively minor position in the hierarchy.

Many dinosaurs were so large that they required great accessory "brains" at the tail ends of their spines to co-ordinate the movements of massive limbs. (We have similar spinal enlargements for the same purpose, although their dimensions are not as spectacular.) One mammoth lizard, whose bones were unearthed in Wyoming during the 1870's, had a brain the size of a hen's egg in the customary place and a nerve center ten times larger near its hips. The Chicago *Tribune* published a poem in honor of the lizard:

> You will observe by these remains
> The creature had two sets of brains . . .
> If something slipped his forward mind,
> 'Twas rescued by the one behind.

The dinosaurs were not dim-witted animals, which passed because of the coming of a superior intelligence. Creatures with horn-rimmed spectacles were still a long way off. The oversized reptiles survived more than eighty million years and we have yet to prove that we can do as well. Their main weakness was their blood not their brains. They had no way of regulating the temperature of their bodies. Like mad dogs and Englishmen, they went out in the midday sun. Tropical climates kept their blood warm, and there was plenty of food to provide energy for roaming about the jungles. But during colder times the masters of the land became as sluggish as hibernating bears. When extra-severe geological upheavals produced rising continents and falling temperatures, jungles and dinosaurs disappeared together.

Man's early ancestors were mammals distantly related to the present-day African elephant shrew, which has a trunklike be-whiskered nose and resembles a cross between a mouse and a baby kangaroo. With Tyrannosaurus stomping about, they rarely showed their snouts in broad daylight. It was wiser to crouch in the underbrush, snuffling in the dirt for worms and insects. They managed to outlast the dinosaurs mainly because they were warm-blooded. Intelligence came later. Those puny animals are called "prosimians."

They found safety in the trees, multiplied rapidly in favorable climates throughout the world and opened a new era in the history of life on earth.

From fishes through dinosaurs most animals had been guided by their noses. Light doesn't travel far in water and if a fish had eyes only, it would move about as helplessly as a near-sighted person without glasses. Underwater smelling is something else again. It depends on a communications system in which molecules serve as messengers. A fish can detect a tiger shark that lies a considerable distance beyond its limited range of vision. Tiny particles composing the enemy's skin break loose from their mooring posts, float through the water and land on groups of nerve cells specially designed to detect odors. Thus fishes have advance notice of impending doom.

The nose was also important to land-invading creatures, since the particles that are the bearers of odor messages travel through air as well as water. In fact, the first prosimians had what amounted to a nose-brain. The cortex came into being largely as an overgrowth of ancient smell centers. But evolution produced radical changes, which lent importance to an old sense and tremendously increased the amount of information flowing into the nervous system. The shaping of the human brain was proceeding at an accelerated pace.

The sense of smell was far less useful in the trees than down below. Hunting was more difficult, because there were no scent trails. Even if such trails had existed, however, it would have been impossible to follow them through hopeless mazes of leaves and branches. This put a premium on the sense of sight, and evolution took care of the rest. In other words, out of many changed genes, certain ones turned out to be particularly useful considering the trend of the times. Long prosimian snouts grew shorter and shorter, and the face became flatter and less like that of a fox terrier. The eyes moved from the sides to the front of the head. (Like many other processes of evolution, the movement of the eyes is repeated during the growth of the human fetus.)

The retreat of the snout has had its disadvantages. For one thing, it complicates matters when we catch cold and want to get rid of germs. Several years ago Prof. J. B. S. Haldane, the British biologist, was invited to address a distinguished audience of fellow scientists at Princeton University. Professor Haldane caught cold en route to Princeton, and had to blow his nose frequently during his speech—on evolution. Finally, he added a spontaneous and desperate statement to his prepared speech: "When horses or dogs want to sneeze, they have a straight run, but in my case I have to take a hairpin bend. I have no other organ that lets me down so completely!"

However, easy sneezing was sacrificed for the familiar forward position of the eyes. These basic changes, in turn, put a premium on certain types of brain. Animals which happened to have inherited a cortex somewhat larger than the ordinary found themselves in a favored position. In a nerve center once devoted chiefly to the sense of smell, there was room to handle nerve impulses from eyes, ears and skin sense organs. Extra cells were needed to take care of the extra load. Evolution selected the hereditary changes that brought about a swelling, spread-out cortex. Our sense of smell has become an evolutionary also-ran, and by the time we reach middle age nearly half the cells have died in the nerve that runs from nose to brain.

Life in the trees favored three-dimensional vision, improved gauging of distances, the ability to see the form and color of objects in fine detail—and the development of more elaborate movements. Keen eyesight and keen interest came together. The branch of a tall tree provided an ideal perch to observe, with little risk, saber-toothed tigers, wolves and other ferocious animals fighting one another to the death. Prosimians were probably the world's first spectators. Secure in their balcony seats, they watched and learned while others killed. They stayed in the trees for about fifty million years.

We do not know why some of the prosimians came down to earth. It may have been sheer curiosity. Or another change of climate may have wiped out large stretches of forest and forced an exodus from the trees. In any case, the creatures were already near the top rung of the evolutionary ladder. Recent theory does not jibe with the "missing link" notions of the 1920's. There was no monkey stage between prosimians and the first ape-man that walked upright. Monkeys evolved from prosimians and remained monkeys. Orangutans, chimpanzees and gorillas came from the same stock at about the same time—about fifteen million years ago —and remained orangutans, chimpanzees and gorillas. The same stock produced early man.

Throughout this period evolution continued to put a premium on a larger and larger cortex. A motion picture condensing ages of hereditary changes into a few reels would show nerve cells rising from deeper parts of the brain, taking up positions at the surface, and starting to spread out for more living space. A tide of gray matter would be seen flowing and completely burying underlying centers. In us the cortex not only covers the entire surface, but folds down into the deepest convolutions. More than two thirds of the human cortex lies in the natural crevices, much of it still tucked away where the instruments of the neurosurgeon rarely penetrate. A great deal of it is devoted to the association areas, where many kinds of information are pooled and analyzed.

Exploring the Cortex

This is the "new brain" which, according to one point of view, represents the site of all uniquely human qualities. It is the thickest and most densely overgrown part of the cerebral jungle, containing regions as mysterious and inaccessible as vast stretches of the earth were a few centuries ago. No single scientist or group of scientists can understand the whole cortex, and it may take years to explore an area no bigger than a postage stamp. Specializing in research has come in for a great deal of criticism recently, because it produces strange technical jargons and people who find communicating with one another increasingly difficult. But there is no other way to study things as complex as the cortex.

Dr. Elizabeth Crosby of the University of Michigan, a leading authority on the evolution of the nervous system, spent half an hour simply telling me some of the steps involved in a typical monkey experiment. Her problem was to trace the course of a certain bundle of nerve fibers. The fibers start somewhere in the surface layers of the brain, and carry electrical signals down to muscles that turn the eyes to the right. En route they pass through, and are hopelessly tangled with billions of other pathways which control other movements. Locating the eyes-right pathway is very much like looking for a needle in a haystack, only more so. At least a needle isn't too difficult to distinguish from a bit of straw, but the nerve fibers of the cortex look pretty much alike and are composed of the same materials.

Dr. Crosby uses one of the standard techniques of the brain investigator. She puts a monkey to sleep with ether, exposes the front part of its cortex and explores the surface with an electrical probe until she finds a spot about the size of a match head. When the spot is touched, the eyes move to the right. The next step is to destroy this clump of cells and wait. Nerve fibers running from the area decompose slowly leaving only a fatty skeleton, a faint "rut" through the depths of the brain. After a few weeks, the monkey is killed and the work really begins.

The animal's brain is hardened in formaldehyde, an ingredient of certain disinfectants that gives hospitals their characteristic antiseptic odor. Then the organ is cut into blocks. The blocks are dipped into a special acid which produces little noticeable effect on undamaged nerve fibers. But when the acid reaches the remains of the decomposed fibers in the eyes-right pathway, it turns them black and "labels" them clearly. Finally, the blocks are imbedded in paraffin and sliced into as many as two thousand sections, each a thousandth of an inch thick. The blackened pathway is followed by examining the sections one by one, "as if you were reading the pages of a book." Dr. Crosby has examined the telltale black stains in tissue sections from hundreds of animals including minks, cats, rats, opossums, parakeets and sheep as well as monkeys.

Sometimes animals escape, with amusing consequences. For example, before World War I there were no opossums in the state of Michigan—until a considerate medical student trapped half a dozen in the mountains of South Carolina and sent them to the university's anatomy department. One evening two of the imported animals, a male and a female, broke out of their cages. A thorough search failed to locate them, and they haven't been seen since. But today their descendants are all over the place, turning up unexpectedly and frequently on the Ann Arbor campus.

Runaway animals are part of the routine of any laboratory devoted to the study of brain evolution. Even without such accidents, however, the risk of tracing nerve pathways would be difficult enough. Dr. Crosby has been at it for more than thirty years, and many other investigators are conducting similar research using a variety of special techniques. The task is an endless one. No scientist expects that the brain of man, or of any other animal sufficiently advanced to be interesting, will ever be fully charted. Attempts have been made to estimate how many possible pathways exist in a cortex containing only a million nerve cells. The number is meaninglessly large. Merely writing it down would fill several volumes, each the size of *From Here to Eternity*—and the human cortex contains ten billion nerve cells, about twice as many as the cortex of the highest ape.

THE OLD BRAIN

Since our behavior is so complicated, it is perhaps natural to identify human qualities with the most complicated part of the brain. But there are indications that the cortex, like intelligence itself, may have been overrated. So far we have focused on the "top man" of the cerebral totem pole, and have ignored the chain of sub-brains underneath. The brainstem and the nerve centers associated with it make up the so-called old brain which plays a major role in regulating blood pressure, breathing and many other automatic functions. It is also involved in raw emotions and all primitive drives.

The old brain has not changed radically since the age of fishes and if we had nothing else, our heads would be no bigger than baseballs. Its pedigree goes back eons before the coming of the cortex. You can see representations of the first "brain" during the summer in tidal pools along the New England coast. The sea anemone (a marine animal, not a flower) fastens itself to rocks, looks something like a stewed apple and has the simplest nervous system known. Its thirteen muscles are controlled by a loosely organized group of fibers resembling a fisherman's net, and its activities are limited accordingly. A hungry anemone extends its tentacles a bit further, waves them about a bit more frantically, and waits for food to float past. Whether or not it eats depends more on the tides than on its own efforts.

Early nervous systems developed in stand-patters like the anemone or drifters like the jellyfish. The closest thing to ambition I ever saw in such animals was an anemone that attached itself to the shell of a large red crab, received free rides and made meals of the scraps the crab didn't eat. This easy sort of existence has its advantages. Waiting for food to float past may not be as risky as it sounds, because the sea is rich in all forms of life. A good many ocean dwellers are quite content to take what comes with the currents and let the rest of the world go by. After all, present-day anemones furnish direct proof that lazy living has some survival value. They are the hardy descendants of soft, squashy things which appeared in the earliest days of evolution.

But the forefathers of the anemone gave rise to another more vigorous line of descent. Three or four hundred million years ago some of these creatures happened to have peculiar offspring. Instead of sitting and waiting, the youngsters swam about and hunted for food on their own—at least during adolescence. Later they developed into adults as sluggish and conservative as their parents. At one point, however, nature decided to try something new. The process took millions of years, but the net effect was that the grownups were scrapped. The adult stage vanished, and only free-swimming youngsters remained to develop into fish with spines.

A nervous system far more complex than the rudimentary nerve net of the anemone and its ancestors appeared with this evolutionary New Deal. Hunting for prey demanded new secret weapons. Natural selection favored hereditary teeth and jaws, fins and tails which made possible high-speed maneuvers, protective bones and scales. Nerve cells were mobilized for greater efficiency. Nerve

612.82   P47

fibers from many parts of the body found their common pathway in the giant cable of the spinal cord. Cells sensitive to light, vibrations and chemical changes in the water were once scattered in remote outposts over the skin.

But in fish they were grouped into large communities, forming special sense organs—eyes, ears, nose—at the front or prow end of the body, the part that bumped into things and usually got into trouble first. The organ that developed to analyze information from the outer world and co-ordinate intricate swimming movements became the prototype for future brains. The old brain represents the difference between an anemone and a killer shark. Life took the offensive, and has stayed on the offensive ever since.

The Brain in Action

What is the relationship between the old brain and the new brain? According to one theory, they are in continual conflict as raw emotion and intellect jockey for control of the body. That seems to be part of the story, but it's far too simple for a full explanation. Emotion and intellect cannot be located and divided quite so easily. The brain functions as a unit. The forces of evolution formed it through the ages. It developed as a servant of the muscles, a way of increasing the chances of survival in a deadly game of hide-and-seek.

In earlier times the game was played by sluggish or awkward creatures. But the interplay of environment and altered genes produced new species with more finesse; hunter and hunted became more clever. Special nerve centers evolved which inhibited gross movements and triggered the precisely timed contractions of small bundles of muscle. The brain was changed from a crude mass-action machine to an instrument capable of marvelously subtle and varied controls. Together with these changes came another which was, if anything, more radical and spectacular—it became possible for higher animals to delay the satisfaction of their wants, to look and wait and think before they leaped.

Something important had happened in the organization of the brain and nervous system. The simplest possible reflex consists of two cells only. A sensory cell carries nerve impulses from a sense organ to the muscles it controls. This two-link chain is capable of fast reactions, the delay being at a minimum because only one cell-to-cell relay is involved. But it is a rigid arrangement. A sensory impulse produces the same reaction as invariably as pushing a button rings an electric bell. Touch a sea anemone, and it collapses instantly like a pricked balloon—and it will collapse in the same way every time you touch it.

The situation changes, however, if an extra cell is placed between the sensory and motor cells. There is a longer nerve chain and a somewhat greater delay. But now the reaction is less predictable; behavior can be more versatile. The added unit is known as an internuncial cell (from "internuncio," an envoy or diplomatic representative of the Pope). It intervenes between sensory stimulus and muscle response, and may introduce a measure of finesse. It may alter routine reflexes on the basis of information it happens to receive from other parts of the nervous system.

You have many such three-link chains in your spinal cord. Usually, your hand jerks away when you touch a hot plate—but not invariably. If you're passing the plate to a guest and it happens to be part of your favorite china set, you may hold on until you put it down. Such restraint would be impossible without spinal internuncial cells. In higher centers like the cortex many, many such cells are placed between incoming sensory and outgoing motor fibers. We take account of a great deal of information from many sources. We analyze, compare, figure out. An abundant supply of internuncial units in the cortex—small cells with short transmitting fibers—provides channels and sufficient delays for all this mulling over.

Consequently, a nerve cell in the brain seldom fires as the result of a signal from only one other cell. Its decision to fire or not to fire is usually based on information from several sources. Usually it must receive all the signals within an extremely brief period, about two tenths of a millisecond (a millisecond, a thousandth of a second, is the unit used to clock many nerve reactions). The cell is so designed that the effects of separate electrical "pushes" must be added together before it discharges.

What you do depends on summations of signals throughout the brain's nerve network. Before eating, you may have to be hungry *and* finish reading that report *and* telephone Mr. Jones. Even when a sufficient number of properly timed signals arrive at a nerve cell, however, it still may not go into action. It delays for about half a millisecond before firing. If during this period the cell receives a "don't fire" signal, it will remain inactive despite the fact that it has previously received its quota of "go ahead and fire" signals. Although your morning's work is done—the report is read, you have telephoned Mr. Jones and you are hungrier than ever— you may wait for the boss to leave first before you go out for luncheon.

We do not know why some electrical impulses prevent a cell from firing, while others act as triggers. But inhibition, which has come to imply something bad and abnormal in human behavior, plays a necessary part in the normal workings of the brain and nervous system. Both inhibiting impulses and internuncial cells permit us to postpone our actions. If a nerve cell's half-millisecond delay period passes without inhibiting signals, it fires. After sending its signal, the cell is "dead" for nearly half a millisecond as it "reloads" or recharges for another burst of impulses.

Evolution has lengthened the time span "between the emotion and the response . . . the desire and the spasm." In us, as in lower animals, the act of consummation is largely a matter of mass automatic movements and the satisfying of basic desires. It is primitive. Once we have food in front of us, reflexes take over. Part of us, the part controlled by the old brain, becomes a robot.

Getting at the food, however, is something else again. For this we need the cortex. A tiger must wait for a while after it sights its victim. Its mouth may water and it may tremble in anticipation. But it does not pounce. Many of its muscles go into action; many more are inhibited. Of the sense impressions coming into its brain, only a few are used and the rest are ignored. The cortex is operating with a terrible efficiency. The tiger remembers the features of the piece of jungle before it, and the habits and escape tactics of former preys. It stalks, perhaps for hours.

Our time scale is different; we can wait years or generations for the attainment of our goals. But in the hushed interval preceding the final leap of a tiger are contained all the tensions that in us produce guided missiles and social planning.

Our abstract ideas are probably conceived in the cortex. It has a great deal to say about what we do and how we do it. But it is mainly a top-level consultant. It does not make final decisions. It helps set up broad policies in close consultation with the old brain. And if the old brain is busy with more important matters of day-to-day operations, the cortex waits its turn. The cortex is a bit of the professor, slightly on the academic side. Left to itself, it would speculate endlessly and have little to do with the real world.

Most of the time the old brain nags the cortex into useful activity. It says: "Hurry! Here's my problem—analyze it and report back within a minute!" The cortex replies: "Now, that's an extremely interesting problem. It may have some implications you haven't explored thoroughly. I must look into them. It reminds me of . . ." "Hurry—within a minute!" interrupts the old brain.

The old brain drives the cortex. Cut some of the fibers running between them, and the cortex idles. Surgeons do this in frontal lobotomy, an operation used for the treatment of certain severe mental disorders. The scalpel severs nerve pathways carrying messages from lower centers to the front parts of the cortex, and produces significant changes in personality. People no longer feel as strongly about getting ahead as they used to. They still seem to know the rules and strategies of their respective games. But they are perfectly content to live without improving their skills or competing with others. The old brain represents whatever it is that makes us desire and care.

BRAINS OF THE FUTURE

The human brain has come a long way since the sea anemone, and it is still evolving. Fossil remains show that the brains of horses, whales, deer and other mammals became larger during the course of their evolution. Most investigators expect a similar growth record for man. Adults with swollen brain-cases holding perhaps as much as an extra pound or so of gray matter will look a good deal more like children, because their heads will be much larger in proportion to their bodies. Learning will take longer. A monkey runs when it is two weeks old, while a child requires eighteen to twenty-four months. Professor Haldane predicts that the man of the future "will not speak until he is five years of age and will continue to learn until he is forty."

The most easily educated areas of the brain, the ones whose detailed structure is least determined by heredity, will grow more than any other parts of the nervous system. These areas allow for the greatest variety of activities and ideas, and have expanded most rapidly in the past. Furthermore, certain nerve centers concerned with instinctive, automatic behavior are shrinking in size. As far as we can tell from the changing anatomy of the human brain, the men and women of the distant future will be even more difficult to regiment than they are now. The chances are exceedingly slim that we will freeze into the sort of system evolved by the so-called social insects. Ant brains have about 250 nerve cells, bee brains about 900. We have 13,000,000,000. *Brave New World, 1984* and other novels that picture future races of semi-zombies may make good reading; they are very poor science.

The prospect of bigger brains has led to another dismal prediction. According to one theory, the nervous system is a kind of creeping ivy on the human frame, a parasite that has been growing fat on the rest of the body. It already uses up about 25 per cent of the oxygen you inhale (about twice as much as the oxygen requirements of ape-brain), and may be interfering with the workings of organs much more important as far as survival is concerned. The high incidence of stomach ulcers, high blood pressure and other diseases that flare up during emotional stress is cited to support the notion that our enlarging brains may kill us.

It could happen. But the argument sounds too much like the old tale about the saber-toothed tiger, which is supposed to have become extinct because its teeth grew so long that it could not bite effectively. Actually, it survived for nearly forty million years and when it vanished during the last Ice Age, it could still bite effectively. The Irish elk whose antlers grew too large for his head and the oyster with shells that curled so much it couldn't open are also evolutionary myths. There is no evidence that any creature has died out because a part of its body was overgrown. If we become extinct, the odds are that the size of our brains will have nothing to do with it.

Three possibilities are open to Homo sapiens. He may be replaced by another species, disappearing altogether or continuing as a "poor relation"—an animal which almost made it but not quite, like the chimpanzee or gorilla. What sort of animal could replace us? It will not be a strange breed of microbe or insect—these organisms have had their day, and evolution never gives a species a second chance. It might be an advanced type of ape or one of the living prosimians, like the large-eyed lemur. But we have no clues.

If an observer had been asked a similar question in the days of the dinosaurs, his guess would almost certainly have been wrong. No one could have foreseen that the species of the future would evolve from the ratlike creatures which quivered with fear as monster reptiles thundered by. The problem is just as difficult today —assuming, of course, that the species exists. If it's to be a new species, guessing is even more difficult. One scientist points out that "there are no truly aerial . . . organisms living and reproducing in air . . . as seaweeds and fishes do in water."

Another possibility is that we may wipe ourselves out. Anyone acquainted with recent work on self-guiding missiles designed to carry atomic warheads cannot keep the prospect out of his mind. About the only positive thing that can be said along such lines is that no other species has been able to accomplish the feat. Nature has always done its own scrapping of species.

Finally, and this has never happened either, we may be the animal that survives—and keeps on evolving. Most long-lived species that are with us today represent evolutionary dead-ends. Some of them found their niches, settled down and have reproduced practically unchanged for as much as 400,000,000 years. The tendency is strong in even the most highly advanced animals. Give a chimpanzee, a few chimpanzees, a peaceful stretch of jungle and plenty of bananas, and it will live happily for the rest of its life. Give a man an environment correspondingly idyllic, say a Garden of Eden, and he will get into trouble. Getting into trouble is our genius and glory as a species.

Of all animals, we are the only ones with brain sufficiently complex to keep us in a constant state of "maladjustment." We are always trying to go to places where we have never been before— the New World, darkest Africa, the North Pole. Our drive toward the planets and the stars is in the grand old tradition. The first creatures that came out of the seas and flapped about experimentally on a primeval shore were great pioneers. But they stopped there, and left further advances to other species.

Our Christopher Columbuses and Daniel Boones keep coming. We keep inventing new devices, new desires for the devices to satisfy and new ways of arousing those desires. We design radar, radio telescopes and other instruments which extend our range of vision by millions of light-years. And we organize the search for new problems into a full-fledged profession. Science with its appalling output of more than a million technical papers a year is a sophisticated method of discovering things too complex for our brains to analyze. Then we build electronic calculating machines, accessory brains, to help us.

Evolution seems to have put an extra energy supply somewhere in the old brain, cortex and their interconnecting fibers. It has been called everything from keeping up with the Joneses (which, of course, means getting ahead of them) to divine discontent. It may be enough to make us the first exception to the iron-clad rule that nature either "freezes" her species, or else discards them entirely.

3

FROM BIRTH TO OLD AGE

THE result of half a billion years of evolution is achieved during the nine-month span from conception to birth. A single egg divides into two cells, the two divide into four, and so on. Enormous numbers of cells are produced, every one of them being developed for definite duties. Muscle cells do work, bone cells form columns of natural concrete, blood cells bring food to the tissues and take away wastes. These specialists migrate across unfamiliar territory to their appointed posts as unerringly as homing birds. Some twenty-six trillion cells have been created by the time an infant is born, including those that make up the brain and nervous system.

Nerve cells are unique, and not only because of the fact that they are living batteries, electrical signaling devices. They are sterile as any hybrid. They cannot reproduce. The rest of the body's building blocks are replaced when they die. When you cut your finger, for example, skin cells respond to the emergency by multiplying and producing fresh generations to fill the gap. But a destroyed nerve cell is gone forever. You will get no new ones. The ten billion cells in your cortex were created four months *before* you were born, and that supply has to last for the rest of your life.

If all basic units are present at birth, how does the brain develop? What grows as the brain becomes larger? The cells are there, but many of the fibers which will connect them have not yet grown to their full extent, or are not functioning. In a sense, a human infant is a lower animal when it is born. It has a cortex, but the fibers between cortex and lower brain centers do not conduct messages. On the other hand, important duties are being performed, or else the infant could not survive. Its heart beats; it breathes, swallows, sucks.

This means that certain nerve cells are already connected in just the right way. Automatic reflexes imply the existence of fairly well-laid-out nerve pathways. In other words, some of the 30,000 genes we inherit from our parents have been at work directing certain details in the construction of the brain. We do not know how many genes are involved in the task, but it must take a good many of them. At least 150 are required to build the eyes alone, and that does not include the genes which control eye color. So the entire brain must call for perhaps a thousand or more genes. But even if all our genes were devoted to shaping the brain and nervous system—and had no other duties—they could determine the connections among a mere ten thousand nerve cells.

Since we have billions of such cells in our heads, we can inherit only the general organization of our brains. Large areas are "sketched out" roughly. They are ready to be shaped by experience and to change, rapidly and continually, under the influence of increasing knowledge. Relatively unalterable nerve nets take care of our reflexes. Flexibly organized structures whose patterns shift throughout life are required for learning, imagination, discovery. One of the mysteries of growth is how an organ combining these qualities can be formed from a tiny blob of protoplasm. This chapter will discuss early development, the impact of experience and some of the changes which take place as we grow older.

From Egg to Infant

An unfertilized egg leads a quiet and relatively uneventful existence. It uses up extremely small quantities of oxygen, and shows about as much activity as a vegetable. But it is very much alive. A sphere only a few millionths of a cubic inch in volume, it contains most of the raw materials needed to start the production of a human infant. The egg is a pinpoint of biological possibilities, a capsule packed with raw materials and chemical regulators that can mold the raw materials into tissues and organs. The product has been designed; the equipment and power-supply are ready. All that is needed is something to set the whole system going.

That something is the tadpole-shaped sperm that succeeds in penetrating the tough outer coating of the egg. It releases the most spectacular burst of living energy known, a chain reaction of splitting cells and rapid cycles of chemical reaction. In fact, the reactions unleashed by the arrival of the sperm take place at such a breakneck pace, biologically speaking, that nature is continually applying the brakes to prevent things from getting out of hand. If the body grew as fast after birth as before, even at the greatly reduced rate of the last fetal month, a full-grown adult would weigh more than ten million suns and his waistline would be measured in astronomical units.

Your brain began taking shape when you were minus eight and a half months old and about a twenty-fifth of an inch tall. The earliest trace of the nervous system is a raised area or plate on the surface of a water-filled ball, the human embryo. The edges of the plate grow higher and a portion along the centerline sinks, forming a narrow groove. As the groove becomes deeper and deeper, the petal-like edges curl upward and around toward one another. Soon they touch and fuse into a closed tube.

The nervous system is rushing through its own private evolution which in broad outline duplicates the great sweep of evolution on a large scale. Each second of embryonic life represents developments that took centuries during past geological ages. By the time it has reached the tube stage the human nervous system roughly resembles that of the ancient marine worms, the humble ancestors of all creatures with spines. The brain of a five-week-old embryo has already advanced two hundred million years or more. The so-called neural tube is bent in the form of a question mark, and a "blister" at the end of the hook is destined to become the cerebral hemispheres. If our brains stopped growing at this stage, we'd rank with primitive fish on the I.Q. scale.

Within another week or so the embryo has leaped ahead another hundred million years. In human growth as in evolution the old brain is already fairly well developed when the new brain or cortex makes its debut. The cortex orginates as a thin film of gray tissue which spreads over the uppermost surface of the growing brain. From the third month on it becomes thicker and covers a larger and larger area. Before birth the brain in general, and the cortex in particular, grows faster than the other organs of the body as far as sheer bulk is concerned.

Such rapid development is the prelude to birth. Dr. W. Grey Walter, a leading British brain investigator, has described the process as follows: "The convulsive twitching and stretching of the unborn child is evidence that its oxygen supply is lagging behind its needs; with growth the deficit increases . . . until, at the appointed phase of some maternal tide, half suffocated, the baby thrashes its way to freedom or disaster. So, too, the pulsations of a jellyfish, augmented in the breathless oily calm of a summer sea, drive it toward regeneration in the foam of breakers."

Order out of Chaos

Considering the nature of early growth, it is no wonder that newborn infants look a bit top-heavy. After all, a large proportion of their weight is concentrated in their brains—which is just as it should be considering what lies ahead. It is a popular notion that being born is the most catastrophic event of our lives. Adolescence, getting married, being drafted, retiring are considered minor matters compared with our violent introduction to human society. A baby passes from a place of peace into a bedlam of noises and lights and shadows, a chaos of nerve-bombarding sensations. The shattering experience is supposed to leave deep and permanent scars on the mind.

But a different interpretation is also possible. Nature protects babies by exposing them to the facts of life step by step, in small and slowly increasing doses. Their nervous systems are designed so that at first they receive only a minimum of sensation, and can take their time about piecing things together into a meaningful picture of the world. They may be resilient and adjustable to an extent that grownups can hardly appreciate. In fact, birth may be more of a shock to the parent than to the newborn infant.

In any case, the experience—whatever its impact—cannot be described. For one thing, we cannot remember because our faculties are not sufficiently developed at the time. Not long ago there was a wild orgy of recollecting among a group of people who called themselves dianeticists. After reading up on psychoanalysis, among other subjects, they succeeded in out-recollecting the Freudians. Unearthing memories of infancy and early childhood was too superficial, and serious attempts were made to probe much deeper into the earliest stages of life. Out of these attempts came strange remembrances of things past, memories of events that supposedly took place before birth and—in some cases—even before conception. Such claims do not jibe with what we know about the brain.

Memory involves specific objects and clear-cut events, and the infant's earliest days are times of vague and limited sensations. It takes time before the nature of things begins to make sense, before vague forms appear in true perspective—and how fast we discover the world depends to a large extent on the growth rate of the brain. Certain nerve fibers which connect the brain with other parts of the body are already formed at birth. But they are not ready to carry messages.

Bare wires may conduct electricity poorly, because the current may leak away before it reaches its destination—and some of the most important fibers in the infant's nervous system resemble such faulty wiring. These fibers do not work efficiently until they are "insulated" by a fatty white substance which creeps along the nerve channel, forming a tight-fitting sheath as it goes. Although the process continues for many years, it is most rapid during infancy and childhood. The insulating substance advances from the head end of the body downward and whenever it completes nerve connections, some part springs into action as if touched with a magic wand. The eyes begin functioning before the arms, hands and legs. A baby sees objects before it can reach out to break them, and it grasps before it walks.

Making sense of things is a gradual process which we cannot

recall. But we can guess at what the process was like, and certain medical records may provide some idea of the troubles we had. What happens when persons blind from birth have their sight restored surgically? If we are to believe Hollywood melodramas, the heroine sees as soon as the bandages are removed—and sees clearly enough to fall in love with the rising young surgeon who happens to be standing close at hand. Unfortunately for the scriptwriters, it doesn't work out that way in real life. The experience is anything but pleasant; in fact, it may have tragic consequences.

Here are the words of a girl who saw for the first time at the age of seventeen. "The light hurt. I wanted to run away and hide in a dark place. All I could see were colors and flashes that wouldn't stop. The way I was before seemed like a delicious rest." For months she couldn't enjoy her garden, or even find her way around in it, without first closing her eyes tight to shut out the confusing light. Friends she once knew by the sound of their voices became strangers, as she tried to recognize them visually. The girl finally learned to use her new sense, but she needed psychiatric help before she could do it.

Other patients have had similar difficulties. One eight-year-old boy spent more than three weeks studying his first picture book. During that period he learned to identify all the objects illustrated. But when the same pictures were presented again, this time colored differently, he couldn't recognize any of them. A young man was able to recognize an egg, a potato and a lump of sugar under regular white light—but not under yellow light. The two patients tried to identify objects by color mainly, a common tendency among such cases. They were frustrated time and again until their eyes and brains became accustomed to shape, size, position and all the other factors that we take into account without thinking about it.

Of course, the process is not exactly the same in infants as it is in older persons. An infant has no long-established habits to change, and there are other differences. But these case histories furnish indirect evidence for an important fact—even the most "obvious" things have to be assimilated gradually. They are not built into us at birth. We are born with the basic apparatus for knowledge; the rest is up to us and society.

The world takes shape for the growing child as parts of its brain are altered by experience. We have seen that the brain is subjected to an unceasing barrage of messages coming in from sense organs through sensory fibers—and that we act because of messages passing out of the brain through motor fibers which lead to the muscles. But nothing has yet been said about what goes on between sensation and action, among the "internuncial" cells located between sensory and motor cells. One of the things that goes on is learning and, according to the limited evidence available at present, this process may take place somewhat as follows.

Most learning is the result of repetition, experiences registered over and over again. In other words, it is a kind of exercise and the brain is something that tends to improve with use. The same thing goes for the muscles. Exercise makes them bigger, but not by increasing the number of muscle cells. A clerk and a stevedore of the same general build have the same number of muscle fibers in their biceps, although the clerk's most strenuous task may be tugging on a stuck file-cabinet drawer. Exercise increases the size of individual muscle fibers, particularly the unused ones that are limp and shriveled.

Similarly, learning does not increase the number of cells in the brain, which is set once and for all at birth. But there is some evidence as to how it affects individual nerve cells. Repeated impulses through nerve fibers in the brain of a growing child may stimulate the fibers to grow extra branches, extending "feelers" which make new contacts with other nerve cells. Ramón y Cajal, the Spanish anatomist who won the 1906 Nobel Prize for his brain studies, once compared the brain to a garden full of trees "which, in response to intelligent cultivation, can increase the number of their branches, strike their roots over a wider area and produce even more varied and more exquisite flowers and fruits."

The beginnings of learning are not spectacular. Little Johnny burns his tongue on a piece of food and his mother says something about the food being too hot. If "hot" is a new word, he may have further encounters with food that hurts before he knows what it means. He will learn the alphabet and identify certain letters with the sounds that stand for the sensation. He will learn to write the letters that stand for the sounds. He will find that burning matches, embers and the sun are not only hot but red—and that redness may be a sign of violent activity among the atoms composing hot objects.

Gradually the network of our ideas—and the network of nerve fibers connecting brain cells—becomes more and more intricate. Sooner or later Johnny will associate red with powerful emotions and certain political faiths. We never stop relating things, even in sleep. Our dreams are elaborate sequences of associations, and may be an important source of new patterns. We are continually making connections among ideas and "making connections" can be taken quite literally, in the sense that learning may bring about new pathways among the nerve cells in the brain. If the cells are in constant motion, as suggested by recent studies, the activity may be a result of the learning process.

All this goes on in the cortex or new brain, particularly in the unmapped association areas where many messages are pooled to form patterns among cells. The cortex and our awareness of the world develop together. At birth the entire brain of an average male infant weighs eleven to twelve ounces, about the same as the brain of an adult chimpanzee. By the age of two it weighs more than two pounds, and the cortex begins a new period of rapid development. Between two and six the cortex completes the major part of its growth, a fact that jibes nicely with theories concerning the importance of early-childhood experiences. But it continues developing at a slower rate for many years, and the final stages may occur as late as middle age.

Locating Yourself

The brain, as a master governing center, is concerned with domestic as well as foreign affairs. Out of all the sensations that flood into the nervous system of a child, some come from the environment and some arise within its own body. The brain recognizes the difference and sorts one from the other.

The cortex deals largely with the relations between you and the outside world, between the body and its surroundings. Injury to certain areas may produce strange effects. Our notions about the positions of things may be turned topsy-turvy, and finding our way around becomes hopelessly difficult. It's as if you were living in a room with the floor going at crazy angles and trick mirrors, like the amusement-park sideshow known as The House That Jack Built. One woman found that her apartment had become a maze of nightmare alleys, as she stumbled over familiar pieces of furniture and confused right- and left-hand turns. Sometimes she couldn't get out of a room. Sometimes she entered rooms she had no intention of entering. The patient was not blind. Space was distorted for her because of damage in visual areas or maps at the back of the cortex. Such cases indicate the importance of the new brain in forming our picture of the outside world.

But nerve centers tucked away in the old brain underneath the cortex deal with the relations between you and your private inner world, between the body and itself. They grow with the cortex, in evolution and in the course of a lifetime, and play a major role in our awareness of ourselves. They are the physical expression of all the meaningful notions included under the broad heading "ego."

During the war Dr. Paul Yakovlev of the Harvard Medical School made a striking observation on how these primitive centers may work. Late one afternoon he was making rounds in a mental hospital near Boston and happened to notice two patients as he passed. At first glance there was nothing unusual about the scene. One patient was lying down and the other was sitting calmly by the bedside feeding her with a spoon. Dr. Yakovlev turned away to continue his rounds. Suddenly he turned back as he remembered something about the patient who was doing the feeding.

He knew that patient. She was thirty-seven years old and was suffering from a nervous disease that made it extremely difficult for her to move about. She couldn't speak clearly or perform the simplest actions necessary to take care of herself. She couldn't dress herself in the morning or undress herself at night. In fact, now that he was thinking about it, Dr. Yakovlev recalled that he'd seen the woman in the dining room earlier that same day—being fed by one of the nurses. This was a patient who was utterly unable to feed herself. Every time she tried, her hand trembled so violently that she couldn't get the food into her mouth. Yet here she was, feeding someone else and doing a good job of it.

Dr. Yakovlev soon realized that he was seeing a particularly vivid demonstration of something psychiatrists had been speculating about for a long while. Eating is an activity that calls on the brain to serve the individual in which it is housed. Scooping a bit of meat off a plate, moving your arm upward, opening your mouth—these movements involve elaborate relationships among various parts of the body to satisfy a need of the body. The patient's disease was affecting the nerve centers which deal with the inner world, so she was unable to feed herself or manage her personal affairs. But her cortex was intact and she could help fellow patients with their meals. Dr. Yakovlev is a practical physician as well as a theoretician. It was wartime and there was a shortage of nurses and orderlies. The woman and similarly afflicted patients who couldn't feed themselves were encouraged to feed each other.

A whole complex of bunched-together nerve cells is required to attend to the unique problems of the private world. The complex includes the *basal ganglia*. These islands of gray matter are buried in the white matter of the cerebral hemispheres and have an ancient pedigree. In the distant past the highest forms of life on earth were creatures that could live on land and in water. Their brains contained a gray mass of nerve tissue, shut tight inside like the core of a golf ball.

Then evolution branched off in two directions. Both branches deserted the water and pioneered in extending the frontiers of life. One branch developed into birds, nature's most advanced experiment in aeronautics. Flying demands relatively light bodies and severely restricts the size of the brain. In birds the central gray core stayed put and, within its cramped quarters, became an ingenious mechanism and the main part of the nervous system. It regulates such marvelously complex but automatic activities as nest-building and homing.

Representatives of the other evolutionary branch ultimately learned to fly, too, but they took a roundabout route. This branch, leading from reptiles to mammals and apes, stayed on dry land where greater bulk was possible—and developed intelligence and other qualities that find their highest expression in man. One feature of the development was that the central gray core broke out of its cubbyhole. Nerve cells migrated to the top of the brain, where they found plenty of room for expansion and formed the new brain—a process which is repeated in the human embryo. The basal ganglia are remnants of the primeval core.

As already emphasized, these centers take care of those activities which were once learned and are now carried out automatically. They control the things you do without thinking or paying attention. Tying neckties and shoelaces, eating, driving a car—these and many other activities once required a good deal of trial and error to learn. In other words, they may have once involved your cortex and have now been delegated to the basal ganglia. The highest center first works out the details of a new action, times the steps in the proper order and plans a schedule of operations. Then it somehow seems to pass the whole program downstairs, to the basal ganglia below. Incidentally, injury to certain of these buried gray masses may produce a characteristic loss of volition or will power. A patient on his way to dinner may slow down and stop in his tracks. He knows where he was going and he is still hungry. But he does not have any desire to continue walking. He needs frequent pushing.

Even more interesting, the basal ganglia may have a good deal to do with thinking turned inward and the entire notion of the self. They are strategically situated near one of the brain's key crossroads, where signals from the cortex and outer world come together with sensations from the inner world of the body—nerve impulses from muscles, joints and internal organs. What evidence exists to back the theory that these centers are concerned with our awareness of ourselves? Observations of the cortex, the most "detached" part of the brain, have helped answer this question.

According to Prof. W. E. Le Gros Clark of Oxford University, the cortex often takes an aloof attitude toward the rest of the body, an attitude that shows up most clearly in disease. A patient came into a New York hospital denying that her left hand and forearm belonged to her. According to the medical report: "She insisted that the hand was not hers, that she had found it in her room and sewed it on. . . . When asked what had happened to her hand, she insisted that she had lost it as a girl."

To the cortex, the body may appear to be "it," an object regarded as something inanimate and impersonal. Damage in the cortex may cause a leg to jerk uncontrollably, and a patient is likely to comment on the condition in the following terms: "That leg keeps twitching. It moves on its own. I try to stop it, but I can't do anything about it." Such reactions contrast sharply with those of a patient whose basal ganglia have been injured. He may also suffer from spasmodic movements of the leg, but it is always "my leg" that is moving. "I have to move my leg—I can't control myself." The facts indicate strongly that consciousness of self is somehow built into the twisting pathways and buried centers of the old brain.

THE LATER YEARS

Old and new brains grow up together. As they mature, we learn to distinguish between ourselves and our surroundings and make the best of both. To the infant everything is a great mist out of which vague shapes and sounds continually emerge and disappear like ghosts. Parents and toys, one's own hands and fingers, are yet to be discovered. They must be carved out of the mist by fumbling, bumping into things, getting hurt and being soothed. Each fresh discovery is a momentous event, creating the subtle adjustments and readjustments that are our frustrations and satisfactions.

And all the time new and baffling situations, strange contradictions and relationships, are forcing themselves on the growing nervous system. An infant is hungry. It feels uncomfortable and cries. Sometimes the crying has prompt results; sometimes a long time passes before anything happens. (The fewer such inconsistencies, the more secure the baby feels.) In any case, sooner or later the noise produces magical changes. One of those ghostlike forms looms suddenly out of the mist and comes very close. There are soft sounds, caresses and food. On other occasions, however, crying may have less pleasant aftereffects and the infant is confronted with early inconsistencies in its surroundings.

New desires and problems, or new forms of the old ones, will keep coming throughout life. The process of discovering reality is never completed. Later on it calls for behavior far more complicated than crying for food, but the general sequence of reactions is pretty much the same. Although we may not burst into tears, we certainly stir things up as much as possible when a strong enough urge arises. Although we may not always get what we want, we usually profit by the attempt and hope for better luck next time. Every problem has its impact on the brain. Increasing experience means increasing organization of nerve pathways in the cortex and underlying centers.

The brain is ingeniously constructed to retain its mental resiliency, its ability to form new patterns year after year whatever indignities the rest of the body suffers. It has tremendous reserves, which means that it can operate effectively even though various parts have been damaged. Its "spare tires" are nerve cells ready to take over when others fail. There is no evidence that our most treasured faculties are lost as we grow older. Like other organs, however, the brain changes with age although some of the changes may come more gradually.

The most obvious changes affect the mobility of our bodies. We hear a good deal about how greatly reflexes slow down with advancing years, a process considered to be especially evident among athletes. This widely held notion is not supported by actual tests. Although a measurable slowing down occurs, it cannot account for all that happens. Joe Louis, for example, is supposed to have lost the reflexes that controlled his knockout punch and speed in the ring. But the ex-heavyweight champion's reactions are probably almost as fast today as they ever were. In special driving tests motorists are requested to apply the brakes at the flash of a red light, and the proper response usually takes place in a fraction of a second. The odds are that a middle-aged person will react practically as rapidly as he would have when he was a freshman at college.

What does happen—and what is confused with slowing reflexes —is something quite different. Supposing you are confronted with alternatives instead of a single task. When a red light flashes, you are to jam on the brakes; when a green light flashes, you are to give the car more gas; when a bell rings, you are to press down on the clutch. The characteristics of an aging nervous system show up more clearly under such conditions. A teen-ager can be prepared for several courses of action and shift rapidly from one to the other. But an older person is slower, more hesitant, in making choices under pressure. He finds it difficult to set himself for several possible responses. This is the basic reason for Joe Louis' decreased efficiency in the ring, and for Joe Di Maggio's retirement from the Yankees.

Aging may also affect the cerebellum, the "ball of yarn" attached to the brainstem at the lower back of the head. This is the nerve center which makes it possible for us to maintain balance and posture, among other things. Last summer during a vacation in Maine I saw an elderly gentleman gazing reflectively at a steep cliff. We started talking, and he told me that he had climbed the cliff many times when he was a child. Now even the thought of it frightened him, as it should have. In our later years at least, discretion is sometimes the better part of valor.

Older people tend to be conservative in actions as well as in ideas —and their attitude is usually founded on sound principles of self-preservation. They are often unsteady on their feet, particularly in the dark and going downstairs. A child balances nonchalantly on fence rails, scaffoldings and other places equally inaccessible to its parents who performed similar stunts when they were younger. The parents, having had alterations in their cerebellums and perhaps in other centers as well, imagine themselves in the same precarious positions (possibly with a touch of envy). They turn pale, and either dole out punishments or try bravely not to interfere.

The brain changes in other ways that have not been so thoroughly studied. Why do many older people become increasingly reluctant to keep themselves physically fit? Why are they less excited by games that used to thrill them in their youth? Why do they grow more cautious? These changes are all part of what is mistakenly called "slowing reflexes," and reflect changes in the nervous system—and the rest of the body—which we can only report. We do not understand them. We know that they need not take place so soon and so rapidly as they usually do. All of us have friends who, even at an advanced age, move about with the activity and enthusiasm of much younger persons.

The highest mental qualities change most slowly of all. People in their late forties learn 85 to 95 per cent as well as twenty-year-olds, and in many cases learning ability continues at high levels until the end of life. Memory for past events dating back to early childhood often seems to be better than ever, although it is a well-known fact that memory for recent events may be impaired. (We shall have more to say about learning and memory in a later chapter.) New and original ideas come most easily in youth, but age often brings them to full expression. Although Einstein's fundamental concepts were formed nearly fifty years ago, he has been working ever since to develop the broad theories which revolutionized physics. A few good ideas taking root in our heads when we are young may be more than enough to keep us busy, physically and mentally, for the rest of our lives.

The "longevity" of the brain is all the more remarkable in light of certain biological facts. Your brain actually begins dying shortly after you are born. Nerve cells concerned with the sense of smell start going first, while taste centers are believed to start degenerating next. Of course these changes are so small that they produce no noticeable effects for decades. But the process accelerates with the passing years. By the age of seventy or so the brain may have been reduced as much as seven ounces, which probably represents the loss of millions of cells in the brain.

But just as no one man is indispensable in government, no single cell is essential to the working of the brain. The brain is a system of infinite checks and balances. Between any two centers are a large number of nerve pathways and when a cell and its fibers die, another route may be available. Only a fraction of the vast amount of information that flows incessantly into our sense organs is used for patterning our thoughts and actions. Considerable information is switched off to sidetracks, duplicate pathways to be used in case there's trouble along the main routes. This is our margin of safety, the cushion to take up a large part of the impact of old age.

The Biblical patriarch is a familiar symbol of the limitations which age imposes on the nervous system and the rest of the body. He also represents the wisdom and the persistence and courage of advanced age. His hair is gray. His body is bent over as he walks forward. He needs a staff, and a young boy is supporting him. But he is leading his people into the Promised Land. Increasing research on the nature of old age and on the aging brain in particular will help further delay—and in some cases prevent—the physical and mental changes that come during the later years of life.

4

PATHWAYS OF EMOTION

I⊤ is impossible to describe our deepest feelings. Emotion is a
diffuse thing whose boundaries are as difficult to define as those
of a mist. It involves many parts of the body and produces many
effects at once, so that we experience a kind of broad, over-all impression. By contrast most sensations are quite definite, and can
be located precisely in time and space. When you cut yourself, you
know exactly where the injury is. Sensations are messages coming
from definite addresses and conveying information. Emotions are ex-
hortations. Like sirens or flags or bugle calls, they arouse and in-
cite us.

Emotional reactions are an important part of the elaborate apparatus that keeps us on an even keel, biologically speaking. You,
the "you" that stays roughly the same from day to day and can be
recognized by other persons, are living in a fine state of adjustment. Millions of your cells die every time you take a breath. But
they are replaced as rapidly as they die, because vital chemical
processes continually create just enough reserves to fill the ranks.
This balance must be maintained at any cost. Anything that upsets
it, or even threatens to upset it, may be accompanied by feelings
which in the last analysis can be divided into two classes: pleasant
and unpleasant.

Unpleasant emotions basically supply a drive to put an end to
some situation. A boy passing a graveyard at night may be scared

and walk faster to get away from the place. We are disturbed to various degrees when howling cats keep us awake or guests outstay their welcome or someone attacks us. We usually experience pleasant emotions when restoring biological balance calls for us to prolong or perpetuate a certain set of circumstances. Once the balance is restored, the emotion—pleasant or unpleasant—has fulfilled its purpose and ceases as promptly as an anti-aircraft barrage after an air raid. We enjoy a good meal while we eat it; afterward, we are simply satisfied. In other words, we achieve a temporary calm, a zero position on the meter. All our plans, ideals, scientific discoveries and artistic creations produce brief "resting points of satisfaction" and we proceed from one stage of balance to another throughout our lives.

Not long ago investigators studying emotion concerned themselves chiefly with nerve centers buried in the depths of the brain —as if anything connected with passion would have to be relegated to the underworld. Research was concentrated almost exclusively on the brainstem, although it had long been recognized that the highest structures somehow held things in check. But recent experiments have revealed considerable information about the role of the cortex in emotion and furnish further evidence of the fact that the brain operates as a unit. The following sections indicate how lower and higher centers work together when our feelings are aroused.

The Show of Passion

Some of the most important "emoting" centers of the brain are located in the brainstem—the extension of the spinal cord into the brain. This stalk contains a diffuse system of millions of nerve cells with short fibers, all tightly interlaced into an intricate network. Various compact nerve centers are included in the network like pebbles entangled in a bunch of seaweed, and one of them in particular is of increasing interest to psychiatrists. This is the hypothalamus at the top of the brainstem. It is no bigger than a lump of sugar and represents only about $\frac{1}{300}$ of the size of the brain.

But what happens inside that small volume has a great deal to do with our emotions.

Literally translated emotion means "moving out," and the hypothalamus plays a major role in regulating and determining the purposeful movements of the body. It may prod the muscles into violent bursts of activity and send us roving about in search of food and sex. Also, it adjusts processes of an even more fundamental nature, processes which are essential to our rovings and take place at tremendous speeds. These are the seething, unceasing cycles of chemical reactions that keep life going in a universe of unpredictable change.

The hypothalamus has been called the metronome of the body. It times and co-ordinates the beating of the heart, breathing rates, cycles of sleeping and waking, menstrual rhythms. It measures the ebb and flow of tissue-bathing fluids so that the amounts we take in balance our daily losses. It is the part of the brain which regulates blood sugar levels and body temperature. Furthermore, as already mentioned, it is involved in controlling the breakdown and synthesis of proteins and other vital chemicals.

This central station includes many adjusting devices—for example, a built-in thermostat. When you go out into the cold, your skin temperature starts dropping. The brain is notified by signals flashing along nerve fibers, which start at sense organs in the skin and run to the hypothalamus. The brain center responds by sending signals of its own along other fibers leading to the heart and blood vessels. More blood is pumped to the surface of the body, the temperature rises and metabolism may be stepped up. Skin sense organs send the hypothalamus the equivalent of an "all clear" signal. In other words, there is a two-way communication loop for temperature control—a loop of nerve pathways running from skin to brain to circulatory system, back to skin again and so on. The hypothalamus makes all its adjustments with the aid of similar nerve loops.

We should not be surprised that this center is concerned with emotional reactions. Emotions may be signs of temporary upsets in the balance of body processes for which it is largely responsible.

We are often aroused emotionally when the hypothalamus is informed of, but has not yet made, important adjustments. Its job resembles that of a worker watching a steam gauge or a pilot watching the instruments on an airplane panel. It holds the body's indicators at the proper positions. As long as everything is under control, you are not aware of its quiet routines.

But the instant you are in danger, the instant your wants are frustrated, the hypothalamus is called on for special duties. It receives a barrage of signals when you need food or sexual satisfaction, and when you have to do something about it. It helps raise your blood pressure, increase your heart and breathing rates and produce a host of other changes which prepare you for action. If all you have to do to satisfy your hunger is walk across the street, these changes may be relatively small. If the situation demands more radical measures, however, you may be considerably stirred up. Fighting or running away requires extra energy and the chemical cycles of the body are set spinning at high speed.

Once our needs have been met, the hypothalamus is geared for a new set of special duties. The time for relaxing has come, for easychairs and reading and sleep. The tension of our muscles is reduced. Blood pressure, heart rate, breathing fall to normal or subnormal levels. The processes of digestion, which were inhibited before, begin their leisurely breakdown of complex foods into simpler substances to nourish the tired cells of the body. You are being built up for the needs and problems you will have to face tomorrow.

The hypothalamus partakes in the expression of the cruder emotions that may arise when basic needs are unsatisfied. Acting along with other centers, it can contort the face with rage and fear. It can be disconcertingly "honest" and reveal feelings you want very much to hide. You may blush, sigh or swear in spite of yourself. Often you are not even aware that your emotions are being displayed to others. The change may be quite small, hardly worth noting unless someone has a good reason to. One psychologist describes a card-player who didn't realize that, whenever he was under emotional strain, a blood vessel in his temple would bulge slightly. But one of his friends noticed the sign and used it successfully to call his bluffs at poker. "Mind reading" of all sorts leans heavily on the use of such clues.

Lie detectors, which measure breathing and pulse rates, may provide some evidence of similar involuntary changes. It has been reported that applicants for certain highly secret jobs in the Atomic Energy Commission, the State Department and other government agencies are tested with the instruments as part of the procedure to check up on their loyalty. But not all lie-detector lies are genuine lies. Anger, nervousness and confusion as well as lying may produce similar bodily changes and similar records. Even more important, a man may be utterly untrustworthy in a crisis and yet not know it. If he is sincere and really believes he is one hundred per cent reliable, he fools both the instrument and himself.

At least one prominent scientist will vouch for the following story about a lie-detector test on a mental patient. The patient had convinced himself that he was Napoleon (Napoleon is still a common choice among those suffering from delusions of grandeur, although contemporary leaders like President Eisenhower are increasingly popular)—and he was usually outspoken in his belief. Only this time he suspected that the doctors were trying to trick him. To the direct question "Are you Napoleon?" he replied with an equally direct "No." The instrument, however, indicated that he was telling a lie. In this case the experts knew the facts, but we do not always have advanced information about our own delusions and the delusions of others. This is one of the reasons why lie-detector tests must be interpreted with extreme care, and why the Federal Bureau of Investigation rejects the instrument as being unreliable.

Precise measurement of guilt or any other feeling is still something for the future. Emotion represents the activity of many structures in the brain, and it is not easy to define the special role of any single structure such as the hypothalamus. Some investigators believe that this center is concerned primarily with the marks of passion, visible and invisible. When it is stimulated with an electrical probe, animals growl and bare their teeth as if they were ready for a fight. But there are indications that this anger is not deeply felt. Apparently it is neither preceded by smoldering resentment nor followed by a cooling-off period. The emotion seems to be shut off the instant the probe is removed.

According to one point of view the animals merely exhibit sham rage, stereotyped behavior as meaningless as the gesticulations of a ham actor who knows and cares little about the part he is playing. Certain hospital records support this notion. Brain specialists have reported the case of a Philadelphia housewife who had been growing weaker and weaker for three years. Among her symptoms were bursts of anger which came and went suddenly and had nothing to do with actual events. The illness proved fatal, and autopsy revealed severe damage restricted entirely to the hypothalamus.

Another recent report discusses a more unusual condition, sham mirth. Dr. J. Purdon Martin of the National Hospital in London tells the story of an eighteen-year-old boy suffering from a progressive nervous disease. "When first seen by me he was having an attack of laughing which he was obviously trying to suppress: the laughter was not 'hearty' but was always partly subdued and emerged as successive bursts or ripples." The attack stopped suddenly, and the boy answered questions seriously—only to break into laughter again. The laughing seizures lasted until about two weeks before he passed into a coma and died.

Dr. Martin also describes the strange case of a young man who was seized with an attack of uncontrollable laughter while he was attending his mother's funeral. He left the funeral greatly embarrassed but still laughing. Later he went to his doctor, was sent to a hospital and had one or two other attacks during his stay. He was still at the hospital when he was found in bed one morning suffering from a brain hemorrhage. He died without regaining consciousness. In this patient, as in the case of the boy, laughter turned out to be an omen of death, and the British specialist believes the symptom usually indicates a serious nervous disorder. He also emphasized that both patients suffered from diseases directly affecting the hypothalamus.

Higher Centers of Feeling

The evidence does not permit us to say that the hypothalamus is concerned solely with the expression of emotion, the outward signs of our feelings. It is sometimes a formidable task to determine whether or not a laughing person is really amused, or a scowling person is really angry. The task is even more difficult when the emoting subject is an animal. But this much is clear—the hypothalamus by itself is not sufficient to elaborate the great range of human emotions. Signals from this center do not acquire their full meaning until they reach the uppermost levels of the nervous system. It is in the cortex that events are colored with the brilliant splashes and subtle shades of feeling.

Emotion and passion involve the most primitive parts of the cortex. The structures evolved ages ago among creatures whose lives were more precarious and uncertain than ours. Hunger, thirst and sex drove them into action. Mouth and snout led the way as they hunted, guided mainly by the sense of smell. As emphasized in Chapter 2, this sense has played a significant role in the evolution of the brain. Unpleasant odors warned of approaching enemies and prepared animals to run away—or to stay and fight. Other presumably attractive odors signified the nearness of mates and prey.

Consummation was sudden meetings and pouncings, ripping flesh and uprooted plants, tasting and chewing and swallowing and licking. Life consisted mainly of devouring or being devoured. The cortex that evolved to cope with this sort of existence was hardly impressive. For example, the forerunner of monkeys and men—a sharp-nosed creature that looked something like an overgrown rat—had a patch of cortex which served chiefly to analyze and classify odors. It was probably no larger than a postage stamp. But for the times, the date was about 100,000,000 B.C., that tiny patch ranked as the latest and most advanced structure of the nervous system.

The massive hemispheres of our brains, the bulk of the cortex itself, grew from this ancient seed of gray matter. The original "nose-brain" has not been scrapped. It has simply been shoved out of the limelight and is buried beneath great new centers. But it is still powerful. It is still concerned with hunger and sex, and with the activities of the digestive system. It is still concerned with smell, taste and sensations and movements of the mouth, throat and jaws. And it still participates in our emotions.

One important area of the primitive cortex lies at the base of the brain. You would see part of it if you could look at the under-surface of the brain-floor from below. The rest is folded, extending up along the sides of the deep groove that separates the halves of the brain. The region receives nerve messages from many sources. Sensory signals originating in the heart, lungs, stomach, intestines, sex organs and other parts of the body come to it from the hypo-thalamus. These signals indicate basic needs, small or large disturbances of our adjustments to the environment. Other ascending fibers bring signals from the eyes, ears, nose, taste buds and skin.

All such information is brought together and somehow organized into patterns which represent our emotions. But according to current theory we actually experience emotion only after nerve signals pass out of this region to another part of the cortex, two arching ridges of tissue imbedded in the walls between the hemispheres. Then we may feel sorry or angry or worried. We are prodded into action and usually keep on the go until the hypothalamus stops sending its SOS signals, that is, until our desires are satisfied.

The anatomy of emotion is just beginning to be understood. The active nerve pathways seem to form a closed circuit, or rather a system of closed circuits, like the nerve loops the hypothalamus uses to help maintain body temperature and other vital adjustments. The circuits are extremely complex. They are known to include fibers that run from certain parts of the hypothalamus to the thalamus (an important center for sorting and analyzing sensation) to the cortex, and back to the hypothalamus and brainstem again. Some of the descending pathways form cables nearly as big around as a pencil. The entire system of circuits lies roughly in a vertical position and has been compared to a miniature automobile tire standing on edge.

In a general way many of these facts are not new. For example, it has long been known that an intimate connection exists between emotion and the state of the body's internal organs. It is confirmed every time fear brings a sinking sensation in the pit of the stomach, and every time we refer to a person's intestinal fortitude or lack of guts. The relationship between the sense of smell and emotion is also well known. Psychoanalysts point out that the decline in the importance of this sense has accompanied the development of social standards which demand an increasing control over crude emotion.

But it is one thing to make interesting observations, and something else again to account for them in terms of the workings of the brain. The pathways we have described briefly were discussed in a remarkably fruitful paper presented some years ago by Dr. James W. Papez when he was doing research at Cornell University. His theory about emotion happened to have been prepared in an outburst of emotion, the type known as national pride. He had just heard that a large private foundation in the United States had given more than $150,000 to a British laboratory to study the nature of emotion.

Dr. Papez was convinced that American scientists knew just as much about the subject as their overseas colleagues, and decided to prove his point. Within a few days he had written his paper. That was in 1937. The theory he conceived stands today as a brilliant combination of fact and shrewd hunches. It is not the final answer and new studies under way in many countries are helping to fill in gaps. But it provides a valuable guide to continuing research, which is one of the things scientists expect their theories to do. Moreover, a large number of findings confirm its major points about the role of the cortex in emotion.

At about the same time that Dr. Papez wrote his paper two investigators at the University of Chicago were starting a series of crucial tests. Drs. Heinrich Kluever and Paul Bucy observed monkeys both sides of whose cortex had been removed surgically, including the ancient areas of the nose-brain. The operation produced some startling effects. The animals had been chosen because they were wild and aggressive. When approached, they would scramble in panic to the rear of their cage—and anyone foolish enough to reach out carelessly would have been bitten severely. Now they showed little emotion and could be picked up safely.

The monkeys were abnormally restless, as if driven by an irresistible impulse to examine everything in sight. Furthermore, the tendency was to examine everything by mouth—"biting gently, chewing, licking, touching with the lips and . . . holding the object before the nostrils." The compulsion was so strong that a monkey often bent over and mouthed objects on the floor instead of picking them up. Normal monkeys, like normal children, usually tear to bits anything they can get their hands on. The experimental animals made no attempt to destroy or break an assortment of items such as boxes, a rubber rat, a toy monkey, fly paper and sponges.

But by far the most spectacular change was a fantastic increase in the sex urge. The change was not immediate, usually coming three to six weeks after surgery. Then "the monkeys appear hypersexed, not only when with other animals but also when alone." They indulge in a wide variety of customary and bizarre sexual activities, as if powerful drives had been released with the removal of large areas of cortex. Recent experiments conducted on other animals confirm most of these findings. In some cases cats have attempted to have intercourse with monkeys, dogs and even chickens. In fact, there are records of increased sexual urge in human patients who underwent similar operations for the relief of epilepsy. A few years ago, for example, a seventeen-year-old boy became greatly hypersexed after surgery and attacked nurses several times.

During the past year or so more information about the workings of the older "emoting" parts of the cortex has come from research conducted at the Yale University School of Medicine. Dr. Paul McLean and his associates have stimulated selected areas electrically and produced a whole series of "eating" reactions in experimental animals—sniffing, licking, chewing, biting and so on. Stimulating different regions brings about snarling, growling and other aggressive behavior accompanied by signs of fear or rage. The New Haven investigators believe that their studies provide direct evidence of structures concerned with organizing complex "mouth" activities used in obtaining food and eating.

Dr. McLean has suggested that such structures may be affected in nervous habits that involve the mouth and lips. The thumb-sucking child may be going through a stage when the areas have not yet come under the control of higher centers, and related habits often continue into adult life. Perhaps the person who chews gum most of the day or bites his fingernails or nibbles the erasers off pencils is also a victim of the late development of certain centers or of the fibers connecting them. Overeating, excessive smoking and drinking and the steady use of laxative, sleeping and vitamin pills may also be traced to similar conditions in the brain.

Other still speculative but interesting observations are worth further study. For example, there is a large bundle of nerve fibers which connect the newest parts of the cortex with ancient centers where body sensations are brought together and used to build the patterns of emotion. It is as if the "civilized" cortex were standing guard over more unruly areas which give rise to crude, primitive impulses. Feelings of conscience and guilt may be aroused somewhere near these fibers.

Also, another part of the cortex may be particularly important in influencing sexual activity. It lies in the groove between the halves of the brain, merging with structures that participate in emotional behavior, and nerve fibers connect it to regions concerned with smelling and mouthing. Incidentally, according to some investigators, it is appreciably larger in men than in women —even allowing for the fact that on the average women's brains are smaller. The significance of this difference, if any, is not known so you are free to speculate as much as you want to. But one case shows what may happen if the region is not working properly.

Shortly before the war a fifty-five-year-old woman entered a Wisconsin hospital. She was the mother of ten children and complained that she had been growing increasingly passionate for twelve years. The condition started with vague "hot spells" that passed as suddenly as they came. But she gradually became sicker. Her symptoms developed into the abnormal cravings of nymphomania. At first psychological causes were suspected—until increasing paralysis of the woman's left arm and leg indicated the presence of a growing tumor in the right side of the brain. A tumor was found near the "sex" region in the cortex, and the patient recovered completely after the growth was removed.

These are only a few of the notions currently being considered. They are tentative suggestions based on recent experiments in one of the most rapidly developing branches of medical research. Workers in other laboratories have ideas of their own, and things are at a stage where new discoveries may completely alter present theories. But most workers agree that the ancient cortex which evolved in lower animals is vitally concerned with our emotions. It is not a single nerve structure but a system of structures—and its architecture has not changed appreciably for the last hundred million years. It is basically the same in all mammals from mice to men.

The most primitive parts of the cortex are also the simplest as far as the types and organization of their cells are concerned. It seems likely that they can deal with experience at the crudest level only. They are literally too simple for words, and as a rule our vocabularies do not help much in describing how we feel when masses of nerve cells in these areas conduct signals. Dr. McLean suggests that although the old cortex "could never aspire to conceive of the color red in terms of a three-letter word . . . it could associate the color symbolically with such diverse things as blood, fainting, fighting, flowers." The new cortex with the gift of language looks down upon such activities from a height. Sometimes, but rarely, it manages to express part of what it "sees" in poetry and other forms of literary art.

CIRCUITS OF CONTROL

Emotion has been regarded as an indication that something is out of balance between ourselves and our surroundings. It is a kind of stop-go system for human behavior. When putting things right means we must continue what we are already doing, we experience a pleasant emotion or "green light." Our red lights are unpleasant emotions which tell us to stop an activity that is upsetting our biological balance (or doing nothing to restore it). Emotion and its control are carried on chiefly in structures at three levels of the nervous system—hypothalamus, old cortex, new cortex.

These structures all contribute to the shaping of our feelings. Nerve signals at any level may affect the whole system. If our actual physical needs are strong enough, they receive attention before everything else. If a man is suffocating, signals from his lungs and other organs race along ascending nerve fibers to the brainstem and hypothalamus and then up to the cortex. The highest levels drop whatever they happen to be doing and do what they can to help meet the emergency. But the highest levels can stir things up on their own in the absence of serious trouble down below.

Severe hunger may originate inside the body as violent contractions of the stomach. These disturbances, and the needs they represent, come first. Emotion follows after. The route of electrical impulses in the nervous system is upward from stomach to hypothalamus to cortex. Traffic can also start at the top and flow downward. When this happens, the original disturbance may take place in the cortex, and we have the difference between hunger and appetite. What we desire, in this sense, may have absolutely nothing to do with what we need to stay alive. The sight of a juicy steak or the sound of a dinner bell may make us want to eat, even though we have enough food in us to last for hours. These sensations arise, not within our bodies, but in the outside world. Yet they can produce all the symptoms of intense physical hunger. In such cases, the cortex takes over and impulses descend to underlying structures.

The brain structures directly concerned with emotion are arranged in a hierarchy, like any complex organization. Each level of this super-office has its duties, and all duties are essential to the successful carrying out of its missions. Final decisions and executive orders come from the highest levels, from structures of the new cortex. This means that we are equipped with apparatus for control over what have been called our basic urges. We are not under the absolute sway of uncontrollable drives. Man is not "innately" pugnacious or selfish or anything else—except perhaps teachable.

There is nothing so tenaciously inborn in us, no process so deeprooted, that we cannot modify it appreciably—providing we have good reasons to do so. Most of us do not make a habit of denying our most powerful urges. But hunger strikes and celibacy, which are familiar if not common, show that the strictest denials are possible. If you practice long and hard enough, you can even control processes which normally take place automatically.

Several years ago a Cleveland medical student decided to try an experiment on himself. To find whether he could voluntarily regulate his heart rate, he wrote out a detailed description of his most terrifying nightmare and read the description daily, reliving the experience in his imagination. After four weeks, he found that he could make his heart beat faster simply by thinking of the word "fast" (the nightmare was no longer necessary). In one trial he altered his heart rate from 71 to 180 to 54 beats per minute. Then the student discovered that the pupils of his eyes were dilating and contracting during the demonstration. So he trained himself to prevent that effect while he was regulating his heart rhythm.

This feat of will power was performed in the name of scientific curiosity. But yogis and mediums have other motives, and exert similar bodily controls over longer periods of time to attain their ends. It is no more and no less difficult to influence the physical processes responsible for feeling and thinking. The way we express our emotions and what we choose to emote about represent, among other things, the attitudes and habits of our parents, plus a few we may have picked up on our own. In other words, many of them have been learned and can be unlearned or modified. Of course, some feelings have more ancient pedigrees than others and might be expected to offer more resistance to change.

Being afraid of darkness or falling probably has a long and respectable history, dating back to times of our tree-dwelling ancestors. Even the fear of snakes seems to have antedated the Garden of Eden and notions about sexual symbols. Apes and lower animals have the same aversion. Several years ago the late Bushman, a burly and popular gorilla that used to inhabit the Chicago zoo, created a stir by escaping from his cage. His keeper, however, knew exactly what to do. He obtained a small green garter snake from the reptile house, held it in front of him and advanced steadily toward the gorilla which was squatting under a tree. Bushman retreated in panic to the safety of his cage.

The zoo keeper was no more afraid of snakes (or gorillas) than a burglar is of darkness or a paratrooper of falling. The ways we express our emotions, like the ways we express our ideas, are products of education and experience. If they could not be directed and shaped, advertising would not be so lucrative or political propaganda so important. We can, must and do change. This does not hold true of other animals, which is sufficient to discount broad generalities based on imagined parallels between their nature and ours. After all, Bushman was a representative of the next ranking creature in the hierarchy of evolution. But he had the same fears that plagued his ancestors millions of years ago. It took another species, namely us, to develop the capacity to learn and unlearn beyond all previous levels.

We have discussed emotion as an activity of organized nerve cells, living brain tissue. Some parts buzz with electrical impulses when we are excited or enraged; others take over when we relax. The hypothalamus, a tiny center buried in the brain, helps regulate vital body processes—and is certainly involved in our feelings. But the hypothalamus is not alone. Emotion is a result of events taking place in the cortex as well as in lower centers, otherwise we could never shape and refine our desires. We are now ready to consider some of the more "rational" or intellectual functions of the brain.

5

THE BRAIN IN FOCUS

THE theater darkens. The orchestra starts playing. The rustling of programs dies away together with the hum of a hundred conversations. There are rapid, last-minute adjustments. Coats and dresses are rearranged, hats removed, pocketbooks snapped shut. People shift in their seats, get set and wait. A few of them cough, clearing their throats as if they as well as the actors had to be in good voice. Then the sound of the curtain rising and the throw of a switch. A bright shaft splits the darkness, a sharply focused beam takes the place of the diffuse light that filled the theater before curtain time. The spotlight picks out the star of the play like a pointing finger. The show is on.

The theater has long been evolving techniques for building up suspense, for pulling people out of themselves into created worlds. Music, curtain, spotlight. The entire sequence of effects that precedes the opening scene is a ritual backed by all the tradition of a coronation or a high mass. It has a single purpose—to catch the attention of the audience (and, if possible, of the critics). From there on every stage direction, every piece of scenery, every line of the play and gesture, is calculated to hold that attention. Since you probably have never seen yourself watching a play, motion pictures of actual audiences might surprise you. They reveal a degree of concentration far more intense than that usually devoted to the events of real life.

This is how people with things to sell would like you to sit up and take notice. Your full attention is one of the most valuable and sought-after things in the world. Large numbers of your fellow men devote their careers to the art of subtly hitting you over the head with promises, products, slogans, panaceas and causes, lost or otherwise. Warning signals must be loud and jarring to save lives. Billboards may not always live up to our standards of beauty, or political speeches to our standards of truth. But we are still influenced by them—and often confused. It is extremely difficult being both a good citizen and a good consumer.

Making us stop, look and listen is properly regarded as a top-priority objective. One can have no productive contact with a wandering mind. Some mental patients are chronically unable to concentrate on any subject for more than a few seconds or so. As far as we can tell, they know that something is wrong with them and may suffer terribly trying to get back in touch with people and events that fade and reappear like mirages in the desert. Their ability to concentrate is impaired; their world is broken into fragments. They glimpse the world through knotholes only, and on the run. Attention is the beginning of everything. Given that, we are prepared to join society and to be educated, exhorted and entertained.

Sleeping and Waking

There are all degrees of attention. During sleep it drops to zero —or, rather, as close to zero as possible short of deepest coma or death itself. In a sense you are always slightly awake and always maintain some contact with the outside world. Most people leave a special inner "gate" open which permits us to waken them without much difficulty. The whisper of your name will probably rouse you, even when blaring radios and rumbling trucks cannot. Such facts have inspired science-fiction writers to speculate about "hypnopedagogy," the art of teaching children and adults various courses while they are sleeping soundly. Although a few experiments indicate that limited learning may be possible under these conditions, the evidence is not strong enough to warrant night schools equipped with beds instead of desks.

Most of the gateways to our brains are closed during sleep. The brain seems to need rest more than any other part of the body. During World War II military researchers at Camp Elliott in California decided to find out how long a person can go without sleep, and put a large group of soldiers through a carefully planned schedule. The schedule included some marching, games, extra-large meals, motion pictures and other activities. The men volunteered for this study in experimental insomnia, and were free to call the whole thing off whenever they wanted to. But observers, who soon became highly unpopular, made sure that no one participating in the tests had a chance to steal off for a quick nap.

Several hundred soldiers stayed awake for more than four days, and one set a record of eight days and eight hours! Medical examinations before, during and after the tests revealed no significant changes in body temperature, heart rate or blood pressure. Reflexes were normal throughout, and there was no evidence of muscular fatigue. Sleeplessness has its most important effect on one organ, the brain. The first signs come after two or three days—"increased irritability, loss of memory, a tendency toward hallucinations and illusions." Later certain soldiers developed symptoms of major mental disease. One thought he was an FBI agent on a secret mission for President Roosevelt; another became violent as he tried to break up an imagined plot to kill him. The symptoms usually disappeared after a good night's sleep, but they persisted for several years in two cases.

Such studies indicate that we sleep mainly for the benefit of our brains. An alarm clock is usually sufficient to wake us—and to start a whole series of reactions in our nervous systems. You lie relaxed, breathing slowly, curled up with your dreams. Suddenly the alarm clicks on. Your breathing hesitates or quickens. Your muscles stiffen slightly as if they were being prepared for action. Your head turns and you may roll away from the clock. But there is no escape. At first the ringing is an abstract disturbance that comes from nowhere in particular and has no particular significance. Then all at once you know what the signal means. Your eyes open, you see, and a flood of sensation invades your brain. You are awake and ready for the day's work.

A great many complicated things are going on during this daily transformation. The alarm sends a stream of impulses through the nerve of hearing to the brain. What happens from there on depends partly on a basic property of all nervous tissue, and the following paragraphs are based on remarks of the British brain investigator and Nobel Prize winner, Edgar D. Adrian.

A nerve cell which has been at rest for some time—that is, has not been conducting signals—tends to be sluggish. A relatively strong stimulus is needed to prod it into action so that it fires and flashes impulses along its fibers. After that, the cell is "broken in" and can be aroused more easily. It becomes more excitable. Not only that but it produces a marked effect on surrounding nerve cells, also increasing their excitability.

Thus, the first ringing of the alarm has limited potency only. If that were all the clock did, we would probably continue sleeping. One signal would stir things up in a small area of the brain, but the flurry would die down quickly. We might fidget in our sleep. But the ringing keeps up, and the repeated signals spread and involve more and more of the brain. The noise arouses hearing centers and the disturbance passes on to another area, producing a slight movement. This movement in turn leads to further sensory signals. Impulses from the skin and from stretching muscles reinforce the original signal, and new movements result. The process feeds on its own effects. Each new signal awakens new areas of the brain. The greatest barrage of fresh signals comes with the opening of the eyes.

You do not come to all at once. Your nervous system is aroused part by part, as various regions are recruited one after the other. New facts about waking have been revealed by a most valuable instrument which will be discussed more fully in a later chapter. Large numbers of nerve cells may discharge and charge together in a kind of chorus, producing rhythmical pulses of electricity or brain waves. The waves can be detected by pasting metal contacts to a patient's scalp and wiring them to the instrument, which writes out records of the electrical activity of the brain on a moving ribbon of graph paper.

During deep sleep the record is "flat." It consists of an inked horizontal line, almost perfectly straight. Only an occasional "bump" indicates that some cells flared up for an instant and then sputtered out. But the moment you start to wake up, the record changes. The pen of the instrument starts writing in an unsteady hand. It writes the sort of signature that a person with a slight finger tremor might produce—a series of fine irregular jiggles, twenty or more a second. Such fast waves represent the first twinkle of activity in those regions concerned with attention. If you were suddenly awakened while the rhythm was still present, you would recall feelings of the vaguest sort only: "Maybe I was uncomfortable or something like that. I'm not sure."

This is the first or arousal stage of waking. There are four later stages, each with its characteristic brain-wave pattern. In the second stage slow three-a-second "rollers" replace the fast waves, and things begin to take shape a bit. Your reactions are still vague; you may feel queer. But you can identify crude feelings such as fear or a sinking sensation in your stomach. Stage No. 3 is marked by the vanishing of the slow rollers and the appearance of large, sharper waves or "spindles," about fourteen a second. You are halfway between sleeping and waking. You are really stirred up, and you can express some ideas. You may remember you were dreaming, although you do not know what you were dreaming about.

At stage No. 4 the spindles can no longer be seen on brain-wave charts. A new rhythm appears. The recording pen vibrates suddenly and then stops, producing a burst of smooth ripples. A pause follows in the record; then another burst, and so on. You feel fewer emotions, and ideas predominate. The contents of your dreams come back to you, scene by scene. All the time the bursts are coming closer together, the pauses in between are growing shorter. At the fifth and final stage the brain-wave record shows a continuous series of ripples, the so-called alpha rhythm which consists of ten waves a second. Now, at last, you are awake. Your eyes have not yet opened and you still lie in bed. But, for the first time since you were aroused, you know that it is morning and that you are in your bedroom.

The entire five-stage process has a pace of its own. It builds up a condition of increasing mobilization, a crescendo of readiness, in your brain. The nerve cells of a sleeper can be compared to the individuals in a crowd waiting for a train at Grand Central Station. People are lolling about, and nothing much is happening. Suddenly a click is heard in the loudspeaker of the public-address system. The announcer starts talking. This is arousal, stop-look-listen time. The voice informs the crowd that the train is coming and that the track will be announced in five minutes. The crowd, informed but not yet knowing where it is to go, surges back and forth in a flurry of restlessness as it prepares to wait longer.

As time passes and the five-minute period is almost over, people check to make sure they have their tickets and fold up the newspapers they were reading. The tension is mounting. The crowd is really stirred up now. People are talking to one another. There are last-minute plans and instructions and good-bys. Then the announcer starts speaking again. The final word is coming. The same sort of thing goes on among the nerve cells in your head as you pass from sleeping to waking. This last-minute point corresponds to the time when steady alpha rhythms appear on the brain-wave record—when your eyes are closed and you are still relaxing in bed.

PAYING ATTENTION

But all this is preparation. You are only on the threshold of attention. The announcement of the exact track is yet to come. It corresponds to the instant you open your eyes and focus on some object in the room. This instant is particularly significant, because our eyes take in such a large proportion of the information we obtain from our surroundings. Fixing your eyes on something, looking at it with some concentration, is the essence of attention. As soon as you do it upon rousing from a deep sleep, the odds are that your alpha rhythm will vanish abruptly. It is as if nerve cells were idly pulsing, marking time—only to be snapped into attention by a barrage of messages specifying their individual duties.

Waking-up speeds depend a good deal on what it is that rouses you, in the first place. You may respond at relative leisure to your alarm clock. A warning shout or the piercing cry of a baby, however, can pull you out of a sound slumber far more swiftly than run-of-the-mill signals. Also, some people are naturally slow wakers. That does not mean they cannot really concentrate until midmorning, or at least until their first cup of coffee. They may say so and believe it. But records indicate that their brains are working just as efficiently as the brains of the rest of us. Slow waking is a matter of minutes, not hours. Fast waking is a matter of seconds.

People who claim they never dream belong to a class of peculiar wakers. Of course, they do dream. Wake them up suddenly and you can get them to tell you fragments of their dreams. They describe their dreams in vivid detail when they are hypnotized and asked to do so. "Nondreamers" often spend a considerable amount of time thinking about things they must do next day. When aroused, they pass very rapidly through the five stages of waking, and pay attention to something—an idea or an object—which has to do with the day's work. Before dozing off I, for example, mull over subjects I will be writing about tomorrow, and I usually wake up with the same problem in mind. I seldom remember my dreams.

Whatever your individual style of waking, sooner or later you are up and about. You tend to your daily affairs with varying degrees of interest and efficiency. Yet full attention is a rare thing, if it exists at all. The brain must first be prodded, coaxed and disciplined. We do most things in a relaxed half-attentive state, a kind of high-grade trance. The nervous system is admirably designed to keep us functioning in this condition. Little concentration is required for a host of automatic actions from listening to the radio and washing dishes to shaving and dressing (which shoe do you put on first in the morning?).

In such activities you may divide your attention. There is no reason to assume that the brain can attend to only one thing at a time. When a person plays the piano and simultaneously carries on a conversation, different parts of his cortex are working in parallel. If he strikes a wrong note, he may stop talking and focus more fully on his music—or an especially interesting turn in the conversation may bring about a shift away from piano-playing. But the brain is responsible for performing many duties at once, and there is probably no such thing as undivided attention.

How often do you operate at a high level of vigilance? Driving a car on the way to work, a reasonably hazardous activity, calls for a considerable degree of concentration—now and then. Most of the time you are either thinking about something else or nothing at all. To most Americans shifting gears and steering are actions almost as automatic and unthinking as eating and walking. You know the route so well that it takes a busy intersection or an unexpected traffic jam to snap you into attention. And it's the same story at home and at work. We seldom face emergencies that require more than a fraction of our ability to concentrate. It has been estimated that on the average you spend only about a minute out of every hour doing things that call for anything approaching complete attention.

At the end of the day the brain begins to slow down somewhat. As already pointed out, it takes a stronger stimulus to excite a thoroughly rested nerve cell than one which has seen recent action. In other words, the more a cell is used the more readily it responds to electrical signals. But this tendency holds within certain limits only. It is counteracted by an opposing tendency, fatigue, and tiring cells become increasingly difficult to arouse. Eventually our brains must shut down for the night, although an occasional person has the knack of attending with part of his brain and letting the rest catch up on its sleep. One such exception is Prof. Norbert Wiener of the Massachusetts Institute of Technology, who coined the word "cybernetics" for the comparative study of brains and calculating machines.

As a leading mathematician, Professor Wiener sometimes attends conferences and occasionally dozes off, even to the point of mild snoring. He has been known to break off in the middle of a snore, blink once or twice and then plunge into the thick of an argument. At one meeting in New York he actually corrected a mistake in someone else's discussion before returning to his slumbers. But this technique is not recommended for general use. Although keeping part of the brain awake while the rest is blacked out can be useful, it is by no means infallible. Even Professor Wiener, for example, has been known to wake in vain and make a point that he or a colleague has already made.

In any case, most of us fall asleep promptly and completely when the appropriate time is at hand. Fighting off sleep is a losing struggle. You can postpone the inevitable by slapping your cheeks and shaking your head. But after a while even such vigorous measures fail to help. I tried them during a long and very late discussion when I was gathering material for this book. An investigator and I did not want to doze off, and we gamely tried to keep talking. The conversation did not cease all at once. As time passed, our sentences came out more and more slowly—the hesitations between them, and between individual words, grew longer and longer. We awoke hours later, slumped in our chairs.

What had happened was just the reverse of the five-stage process of waking. When we fall asleep, previously steady alpha waves break up into bursts of waves and then stop altogether. Then there are spindle waves, rollers, fine fast ripples, and finally a dying-out of all major rhythms. Of course, the brain is still operating. It controls basic processes such as breathing and the beating of the heart. Also, we may be mentally active during light slumber; we dream, and sometimes we compose poems and solve problems. But with the coming of deep sleep we are dead even to such things, until tomorrow morning.

Arousal Mechanisms

Certain parts of the brain play a major role in the activities we have been describing. They keep us awake and put us to sleep. They evaluate the relative importance of the messages that enter the nervous system along millions of fibers—and decide which messages the cells of the cortex will respond to. It is their job to direct our attention and focus it, a feat which becomes increasingly difficult as we grow sleepier and sleepier. When we listen intently, signals in the nerve of hearing must be reinforced and signals in the nerve of seeing suppressed.

During the past five years or so many new facts have been discovered about what goes on in our heads when we are alert or lethargic. Much of this recently acquired knowledge can be traced to the pioneer studies of the late Dr. Stephen Ranson of Northwestern University, his pupil Dr. Harold Magoun now at the University of California in Los Angeles and their co-workers. Their research takes us back to the brainstem. More specifically, it takes us back to the tangle of cells with short fibers mentioned in the chapter about emotion.

In us, the network is responsible for many crucial decisions. If you come up behind a friend and tap him on the shoulder, a signal flashes into his brainstem calling for some sort of action. It may or may not be heeded. Your friend may simply turn his head and wait to hear what you have to say. If you have annoyed him, he may ignore you and not move at all. If he thought he was alone in the room, he may be startled. Turing the head is a reflex, and the notion that we are a bundle of interrelated reflexes has something to it. But that does not mean we are merely complicated robots. Our behavior may be unpredictable. A particular reflex is triggered or inhibited depending on what we happen to be doing, thinking and feeling at the time.

We are continually being "tapped on the shoulder" by impulses in the nerve fibers running from our sense organs. Every impulse creates a flurry in some part of the nervous system, which is as delicate and sensitive as a spider's web. Disturb it anywhere and it "vibrates" all over. Obviously, we do not and cannot heed all these signals. If only a fraction of them were relayed to the highest centers of the brain for only a fraction of a second, we would go mad. The brainstem insures that this does not happen. It is a common meeting-ground for impulses originating throughout the body—a place of conflicting demands and interests, of compromises which determine courses of action.

The brainstem resembles a great hall in which a national political party is holding its convention. Delegates from all parts of the country have traveled various distances to voice their problems and demands, and the problems and demands of the voters back home. They include conservatives and liberals, leaders representing labor and business, straight-shooters and connivers, men from farms and men from cities. Deals are being made on the central platform and floor of the convention hall. There are discussions and bitter arguments. Some problems are faced immediately; others are postponed in the interests of party harmony. And out of the apparent chaos, somehow, comes a set of broad policies and a program for political action.

This analogy may furnish a general idea of what happens in the brainstem, providing you do not take it too literally. The thing is not a matter of intangible mental processes, mysterious "little men" who run about sorting and directing nerve messages. The marvel is that such complex and ceaseless activities are regulated automatically by tiny organisms, groups of living cells arranged in network patterns. If you want a more mechanical analogy, think of a mammoth system of superhighways all coming together in one area, all jammed with traffic—and all interconnected at many levels by thousands of overpasses, underpasses, rotaries and cloverleafs. Then imagine that the entire traffic load is handled without the benefit of police patrols. It is directed by automatic switches, operating green and red and yellow lights and tripped by the passing automobiles themselves.

Nervous traffic is controlled in a somewhat similar manner. As a rough guess, about a hundred million electrical impulses pour into the nervous system from the sense organs every second of the day. Some are taken care of in the spinal cord; others pass upward to higher structures. But a total of only a hundred signals—that is, about one impulse in a million—reaches the uppermost levels of the cortex. And only a few of the signals cause us to think that certain events are going on in the outside world. These are the events we pay attention to.

The reticular formation or nerve net of the brainstem is a gateway to the cortex. It "clears" certain signals for top-level consideration. It is connected indirectly with the cortex by ascending nerve fibers which carry impulses from the sense organs. When we are asleep, the number of impulses in these pathways is extremely small. But the first or arousal stage of waking represents an opening of many gates, a release of many inhibitions. Traffic becomes heavier. There is a sharp and sudden increase in the number of signals flashing upward from sense organs to nerve net to cortex. We pass through the later stages of waking as the signals produce more extensive effects in the brain.

The nerve net not only arouses us. It helps keep us awake as well. When we are thoroughly aroused, it is sending a steady stream of ascending impulses directly to the highest centers of the nervous system. Through its descending fibers it also acts upon lower centers which control the muscles, so that they respond more readily to signals from the cortex. In other words, our reflexes are tuned up and prepared for prompt action. This constant background of activity is a major factor in maintaining general alertness.

The nerve net's system of ascending fibers consists of pathways leading to different parts of the cortex—including the areas or "sensory maps" which receive impulses from the eyes and ears. Something special happens when we concentrate. When you listen to an important news broadcast or telephone message, traffic is extra-heavy along the pathways running to the hearing maps of the cortex. Suddenly there is someone at the door. You are distracted from your listening and turn around to see who it is. Now the flow of nerve impulses falls off in "hearing" pathways—and increases sharply in "seeing" pathways. Your whole day is a continual by-play between nerve net and cortex, a sequence of shifting signals and shifting attention. When you daydream or relax or feel sluggish, the level of nervous by-play is reduced along most of the pathways. When you feel mentally sharp, in tip-top condition, the general level is relatively high.

If this intricate system goes out of control, severe nervous disorders may be produced. An abnormally large number of ascending impulses can bring on delirium, mania, convulsion. The other extreme may mean that the patient falls into a stupor. An unusual case has been reported by British brain specialists at Oxford University. The patient was a plump fourteen-year-old girl who had remained practically motionless for weeks. Only her eyes were alive. She watched her doctors as they moved about, and seemed constantly on the verge of saying something. But she did not speak.

The girl had to be served strained foods like a baby. She swallowed whatever was put into her mouth, but she would not chew. It took a minor emergency to make her react at all and, even then, things happened in slow motion. When pricked with a pin, she showed no signs of pain or anger and moved her arm back very slowly. When her feet were tickled, she smiled feebly (before her illness she had been extremely ticklish). She accepted a piece of chocolate placed carefully in her hand. But she didn't bother to lift it to her mouth, and the candy slipped to the floor after a few minutes. The girl was cured by a special operation. Surgeons removed a small cyst or fluid-filled pouch growing near the upper end of her brainstem. Ten minutes later she sat up in bed and began asking questions.

Similar symptoms have been produced by injuring certain parts of the brainstem in laboratory animals. According to one recent report, previously active monkeys "would sit upright in one spot for hours, almost motionless, with an unchanging vacuous stare." But experimental injury does not always freeze motion. Tests on other parts of the brainstem may lead to entirely different results. By tampering with it we can choose our symptoms and produce abnormal restlessness as readily as lethargy. Not long ago an investigator at a large western university operated on a black kitten to prove this point. The kitten came out of the anesthetic purring. It lapped up some milk, played with a bit of loose wire and started chasing its tail. In fact, it was perfectly normal in every way but one. It required no sleep.

After about three weeks the kitten was wandering about as healthy as ever—and, for all we know, it may still be crossing paths in some alley or backyard. One night it vanished, completely and mysteriously. No one knows exactly how it happened, but the kitten escaped from a locked cage in a locked room. Other animals with brainstem injuries behave as if they were driven by perpetual-motion machines. They walk straight ahead in a kind of somnambulistic trance, emitting low cries and never turning aside. One animal walked into a wall and kept pushing with its head; another was placed in a circular cage and kept pacing round and round. Neither animal stopped until it collapsed from exhaustion.

Psychiatrists have seen human cases suffering from the symptoms of this condition, known as "obstinate progression." An unpublished report from the records of a Massachusetts state hospital, for example, tells of a husky Italian patient who ran full force into walls and attendants indiscriminately, and once crashed through an oak door an inch thick. A prominent physician also became overactive following an acute attack of epidemic encephalitis (inflammation of the brain). For months he was afflicted with uncontrollable bursts of walking and talking, and averaged only four hours' sleep a night. Most of his time was spent at bars, night clubs and late parties. He returned to his normal sedate self two years later, as the aftereffects of his infection cleared up.

Such cases emphasize the sort of role the brainstem plays in behavior. We have indicated how it influences the cortex to keep us alert. Of course, no part of the nervous system acts independently. Important fibers run from cortex to brainstem, as well as the other way, and the cortex uses these fibers to affect structures located downstream. The cortex can keep us awake when we are dead tired, when we drive late at night or fight or worry. It can also put us to sleep when we do not need sleep—for example, when we do not want to fight.

But the powers of the cortex are limited. The Camp Elliott tests on sleepless soldiers show that the highest centers are the first to break down as a result of their own sleep-inhibiting effects. If we are to survive, the brainstem cannot be denied indefinitely. It is the hub of the nervous system.

6

REMEMBRANCES OF THINGS PAST

MAGGIE THE THIRTEENTH, a thirteen-year-old chimpanzee, occupies a unique place in the unofficial annals of brain research. She was never brought into a home to be reared with the kiddies and sit up at the dinner table, almost like a human being. She was never photographed wearing a hat and dress, or smoking a cigar. Maggie wasn't the type for domestic experiments. She would have ripped the house to pieces, and been damned as "unmanageable and unteachable" by her victims. But she was intelligent, in her way not ours. Having lived most of her natural life among Yale University scientists, she was wise to the ways of laboratories—and ornery in her wisdom.

In 1943 Maggie was sent to the Illinois Neuropsychiatric Institute in Chicago for special studies. She arrived in an iron-barred crate plastered with "BEWARE" and "DANGER" labels befitting her reputation as the No. 1 troublemaker of experimental chimpanzees. Two of the nation's leading brain investigators, Drs. Warren McCulloch and Percival Bailey, undertook the task of getting Maggie out of her crate. They were forewarned, but not forearmed. Trying a conventional approach, they threw a tarpaulin over the crate and tossed in several pounds of ether. The idea, of course, was that a sleeping Maggie could be transferred easily from crate to cage.

The first ether attack failed. A cautious peek under the tarpaulin revealed that Maggie was as lively as ever. Another dose of ether, another peek, and things seemed to be under control. Bailey turned to McCulloch: "You'd better get her out now. She's lying in the corner." McCulloch opened the crate and reached for the limp chimpanzee. At that moment Maggie sprang into action. Snarling triumphantly, she scrambled on top of a table and defied the gathering audience to come and get her. No one did. The room emptied rapidly, as McCulloch fended Maggie off with a broom. The laboratory door was slammed shut just in time to keep her inside.

From there in it was man against ape. Quantities of ether were poured into the room's ventilating system. But Maggie seemed to have built up a resistance to the drug, because she remained in full possession of her senses. Next a ripe banana was dipped in Nembutal, a powerful anesthetic, and tossed into the room. Maggie remembered that trick. She ate around the soaked part, and tossed the rest right back again. A glass of drugged water was hastily placed near the door. Maggie remembered that one, too, spilling the water into a convenient sink and pouring herself a fresh glass. Finally the chimpanzee's weakness was discovered—a deep devotion to Coca-Cola. A bottle of the drink was spiked with Nembutal, and Maggie gulped it down even though she suspected it might be her downfall. It was; she soon fell sound asleep. But she won a moral victory. Bailey had fallen asleep an hour before, having inhaled too much ether during Maggie's escape from her crate.

Maggie the Thirteenth is still spoken of as the only animal that ever anesthetized a scientist. Her story stands as one more example of the fact that animal intelligence may be of a high order. Given a fair chance animals may conduct themselves quite admirably. In one recent study monkeys consistently outperformed a group of nursery-school children. All the monkeys solved a particularly difficult problem involving considerable memory. All the children but one failed—and the one successful child cheated. As a crowning indignity, an ugly rumor has been circulating to the effect that some cockroaches do better than some college freshmen on maze-learning tests. Many lower species show the ability to remember the past and profit by experience, which is an important part of intelligence.

Of course, there is a good deal more to intelligence than memory.

But at least this ability is something we can study. We cannot observe nerve cells and fibers behaving "intelligently." But we may be able to discover how they do certain more specific things—for example, how they store information and the nature of the memory traces they form. In fact, brain investigators are just beginning to come to grips with the mystery of memory. This chapter discusses possible storage mechanisms in the cells of the nervous system, and presents some recent estimates about the total amount of information stored. The next chapter will discuss how memory may be used to conceive abstract ideas and make predictions.

VARIETIES OF MEMORY

The brain is our main organ of adjustment. Swiftly and continually, the substances that compose our bodies are being destroyed and built up anew. The rate of molecular turnover is extremely high. Memory depends on something that persists through all this, the preservation of substance and structure and pattern in the face of ceaseless change. If we understood it better, we would have deeper insight into other higher mental faculties. Current studies indicate that there are probably at least three types of memory: (1) short-term memory normally used in forming enduring impressions; (2) a memory for skilled acts; and (3) "snapshot" memory for things sensed in the outside world.

The first, short-term variety may be all that is left in the late stages of life. As a tree dies what remains is the old heartwood, which is what the tree was earlier. Much of the past remains accessible to old people, but their ability to store recent events may be impaired. One investigator tells the story of a businessman in his eighties who took charge of an eight-hour board of directors meeting, organizing an enormous number of details for the sale of a railroad. Yet back in his office less than thirty minutes after the meeting was over, he remarked to his secretary: "I have a feeling that I should have gone to a board of directors meeting." He had completely forgotten an event in which he played the central role.

There is evidence that such short-term memory may consist of eddies of electricity in the brain. An event produces nervous disturbances, but not the sort that are relayed from cell to cell in chains leading from sense organ to muscles. These are reflex circuits. The circuits of short-term memory are probably circular. Cell A fires and sends a signal to cell B, which fires in turn and stimulates cell C. But instead of conducting impulses to a more remote point, cell C has fibers which lead back to and "trigger" cell A—and the cycle continues. In other words, a kind of electrical merry-go-round is established in the brain.

An old person remembers a recent event as long as the signals continue to chase each other's tails. The signals can be kept circulating by constantly harping on the event, ruminating, mulling it over and over again—just as you can keep a bicycle wheel spinning by striking it glancingly on the side every time it begins to slow down. The instant the merry-go-round stops, the instant the brain focuses on something else, the event vanishes forever. The eddies may swirl for a matter of minutes or hours, but in old age we form few if any lasting traces.

When we are younger, the eddies also vanish quickly. But before they go, they somehow produce excellent memory traces and we recall recent events with little difficulty. The way we learn skilled acts illustrates how enduring traces may be formed. Such memory feeds on repetition. The more you practice the better you become, within limits. When you get "stale" through overpractice, it is time for a lay-off—and during the lay-off something may happen in the nervous system so that you improve again. These facts are behind the saying that you learn to ice-skate in summer, and to swim in winter.

In the beginning we may be aware of every difficult step in mastering a skilled act. There is considerable trial and error and frustration along the way whether the problem is learning to walk or learning to play golf. It is as if the cortex develops a pattern of synchronized muscle movements, and later passes most of the details down to lower centers, such as the gray masses of the basal ganglia, which—once instructed—carry out actions automatically. The hierarchy of the nervous system is so organized that whenever possible duties are passed from higher to lower centers. Then, if we think too much about what we are doing, we may do poorly. There is the fable of the centipede which stumbled all over itself trying to show how it managed to walk. And the average golfer's game is likely to go to pieces if he pays too much attention to the details of his swing.

We perform many of our skilled acts without thinking, as pointed out in Chapter 3. How do you know exactly what pressure to use when you pick up an egg? Why don't you break it or let it slip out of your fingers, the way you probably did when you first tried? The reason, of course, is that you remember how to perform this everyday act, you have learned to apply just the right pressure automatically. Look in the mirror next time you button your blouse or tie your necktie. Watch carefully and try to describe the entire procedure, step by step. It is too complicated to bother about. The fact is that in such cases you never know exactly what you are doing when you do it. All you know is what you want to do, your purpose. The details take care of themselves or, rather, the brain takes care of them.

Far more complex chains of behavior may be so ingrained, so thoroughly conditioned, that an appropriate signal may set them off in inappropriate surroundings. A veteran prizefighter in a restaurant may jump up from his chair and start sparring at the ringing of a bell. Some years ago John Barrymore was playing *Hamlet* in Baltimore, and went to a local night club after the show. He was dancing when a spotlight played slowly across the dance floor. The instant the spotlight focused on Barrymore (he did not know it was coming), he suddenly stopped dancing and started performing. He gave a stirring rendition of the to-be-or-not-to-be speech.

Such extremes emphasize the built-in, automatic quality of skilled acts. The way they are learned, by being repeated over and over again, suggest that something in the nervous system is growing with use, just as our muscles grow larger with exercise. As already mentioned in Chapter 3, it seems that the fibers of different nerve cells actually grow and make contact with one another when we learn. The fibers do not touch. Their contacts are not the sort made by two wires attached together. They are more like spark gaps across which electricity leaps. Possibly the eddying currents of short-term memory provide a strong enough stimulus long enough to speed the growth of nerve fibers. In any case, it has been reported that fibers in the brains of young persons are not as richly branched as those in older brains.

SURREALIST SNAPSHOTS

Of the three types of memory listed earlier in this chapter, we have discussed the short-term variety and that used in learning skilled acts. A third type is "snapshot memory." This involves a different sort of information coming in through our sense organs, most of it—more than 85 per cent, according to some estimates—through our eyes. When you meet a person, an upside-down image of his face falls on a screen of light-sensitive cells in your eye. If you have occasion to examine his face closely, the image falls on a tiny part of the screen specialized for detail vision.

Chemical changes are produced on the screen and trigger electrical signals which pass along some of the million or so fibers of the nerve cable running from eye to brain. Each point of the eye-screen image is represented by a particular signal, and each signal arrives at a particular point of the highest visual center at the back of the cortex. There is a point-for-point correspondence between the new image and the original. But they are not the same size. The original image is utterly unsuited for the purposes of memory. It occupies an area on the eye-screen about the size of the head of a pin.

If that speck were transmitted "as is" to the cortex, you would be blind to the details needed to distinguish one face from another (or even to distinguish a face from any other roughly oval object). The area on the cortex, however, is hundreds of times larger than the eye-screen area. The new image is magnified for closer examination. Incidentally, this enlarged image is definitely not a portrait. In fact, it is such a poor likeness that you wouldn't recognize it as a face if you saw it. It has been twisted into something that bears no more resemblance to human features than a map does to the country it represents.

The "image" is a strange thing built up of curving patterns which only the cortex can understand and use. If you are one of the persons who can't make sense of some of the more radical experiments in modern art, at least you are free to stay away from galleries. But you can't do anything about the exhibitions in your brain. The cortex is enthusiastically nonobjective. It has no respect whatsoever for "things as they are." The eye sees trees, houses, faces; the cortex transforms them into a rich variety of abstract designs.

The brain has another way of altering reality for its own ends. You see a world in motion. Branches sway in the wind, doors open and close, faces change expression. As far as the working of the cortex is concerned, however, motion is an illusion. The cortex sees "stills" only. It does not view things continuously, but slices the world into thin sections. Its shutters are synchronized with the rhythm of the alpha-type brain waves produced as we waken from a deep sleep. It flashes on and off, taking eight to thirteen snapshots a second (the alpha rhythm, and snapshot rate, averages about ten a second).

Your eyes will take about ten billion snapshots during your lifetime. In between snapshots you are completely in the dark. You are actually blind half of your waking life, only the sightless intervals are so short and the snapshots follow one another so rapidly that you do not notice it. Occasionally we are afflicted with disorders which produce the sort of flicker typical of old-time motion pictures. There are "snapshots" of touch, taste, smell and sound as well as sight. All the information is handled in a similar manner, registered in rhythm with brain waves—and stored in our memories.

One of the unique and interesting things about snapshot memory is the way we may have to refer back to it. It seems to be organized along the general lines of a family album. The snapshots are fixed in position, attached to definite pages, and you have to thumb back and forth through the album to get at any one of them. In trying to recall a face or a scene we may have to think back through many events that took place later before arriving at the point when we had that particular experience. We may have to start at the beginning of a poem or popular song and go through several verses to recall a certain line.

CHEMICAL STOREHOUSES

The brain holds a tremendous quantity of information. One of the most amazing feats of snapshot memory on record was reported recently by a former Yale University investigator. He was studying the well-known fact that people recall things much better under hypnosis than they do under normal circumstances. Among those tested was a master bricklayer who had spent considerable time working on the "showcase" locations of the university's neo-Gothic buildings—interior walls, corners, arches over windows and doorways.

Such work impresses visitors and calls for special bricks which must be matched carefully. Although no two bricks are alike, they must be arranged in esthetically pleasing patterns. The bricklayer was hypnotized and asked to describe a certain brick in a certain wall he had constructed on a certain date. After a few moments, he came up with an answer. The brick had been burned a shade too much in the kiln. It was dark in color. A purple pebble was imbedded in the clay at the lower left-hand corner. The brick had a "belly," a slight swelling, at the upper right-hand corner which matched the hollow of the brick just above it.

The worker's statement included many other details, and every one of them checked with the facts. He had put the brick in place more than ten years ago. Furthermore, he had probably laid nearly two thousand bricks on that same day. Yet his brain had recorded the impressions of a pebble smaller than the end of your little finger, and he furnished equally accurate descriptions of other bricks in other locations. This man was not selected for his powers of memory. Many similar experiments have been conducted, and we still do not know how to account for them. Hypnosis somehow focuses the spotlights of attention on memory traces in the darkest corners of the brain. The odds are that under hypnosis you or anyone else would perform as impressively as the master bricklayer.

Supposing you were gifted with the ability to evoke all the memories in your brain, and sat down with pencil and paper to write them out. You would never complete the list. It would probably never be completed, even if you could devise some way of passing the task on to your children, grandchildren and succeeding generations. And no library would have enough room for the list if you ever completed it. The dimensions of human memory have never been measured, but rough estimates indicate the general capacity of the brain's storehouses.

It is often stated that we forget very little of what we scan. You may not be able to recall every item at a moment's notice but, according to the popular notion, the information is registered somewhere in your head, perhaps in the inaccessible nooks and crannies of the subconscious. Actually, the evidence indicates that we forget more than 90 per cent of all the details of all events, including those which are most important to us. But even so, so much information is transmitted by the sense organs that the amount we retain is enormous. During your lifetime you can store about ten times more information than is contained in the nine million volumes of the Library of Congress.

Memory is preserved in some ingenious way that eludes us still. It is tough and deep-rooted; only death can eliminate it completely. The storehouses in our heads are like great libraries whose shelves are filled with neatly arranged books, old and new. Some are in constant demand and circulate freely and frequently. Memory has its bestsellers, its *Forever Ambers,* and *Studs Lonigans,* its fairy tales and fantasies and biographies and adventure stories. Other books, perhaps the vast majority, are neither interesting nor important. They gather dust on obscure shelves and are referred to rarely or not at all. Masses of information are packed in compact quarters.

Where does it all go? The brain has billions of nerve cells but they are not nearly enough. In fact, if we think in terms of cells only, we would have to conclude that the brain does not have room for its memories. If a single memory—say, a scene or a face or a name—were tucked away in a single cell like a jewel in a safe-deposit box, all the cells of the brain and nervous system would not suffice to hold a fraction of what we remember. As an optimistic guess, they could hold little more than a week's worth of snapshot memories.

The sheer problem of finding sufficient storage space forces us to go deep into the very structure of the nerve cells. Our search takes us into submicroscopic regions where twisted, spiraling long-chain molecules produce the delicate lattice work of living tissue. Each cell is a capsule containing vast numbers of molecules and, for reasons we shall come to shortly, it is believed that the protein molecules among them may be involved in preserving memory traces. These particles, the largest and most complex atomic aggregates known, exist in ample quantities. The brain has about a thousand billion billion of them; one followed by twenty-one zeroes.

We know that a protein molecule can be changed in many ways, and that it can hold its new shape. Furthermore, there is evidence that electrical impulses traveling in nerve fibers—signals representing things we may remember—are among the things that can make the required changes. As the impulses pass, they modify the structure of protein molecules in the nerve fiber itself. According to one theory, memory traces are formed when protein particles are altered in meaningful ways. They bear the marks of our thoughts as definitely as tin cans show dents where they have been kicked.

This may be putting it too crudely and without the proper respect for the workings of the mind. If memory is a matter of altered protein molecules, our memory traces are more subtle things, more like the delicate chiselings a sculptor makes in marble or the epitaphs engraved on tombstones. But now we are confronted with an apparent paradox. Protein molecules have extremely brief life spans. They survive only about a day or so on the average, and then they are destroyed. But this state of affairs hardly jibes with the well-known fact that memory persists for decades. You remember events from your childhood, yet the molecules of memory endure for only a day.

The explanation is that certain giant protein particles can do a most remarkable thing. They can reproduce like living things. To appreciate this feat, try to imagine how you would design a machine to turn out complete machines, each a full-sized replica of itself (theoretically, by the way, such a machine could be built). Your earliest childhood memory once changed protein molecules inside some of your nerve cells, and the molecules were soon scrapped. But before they passed they left offspring—and the offspring had the same markings as their parents. In other words, protein molecules representing the memory of something that happened when you were a child have been multiplying or "breeding" ever since. This process may go on for sixty years or more, each generation of new molecules replenishing the old supply and preserving memory traces.

It should be emphasized that, as far as we know, only giant proteins can manufacture images of themselves. Some investigators are convinced that the substances will be definitely identified with memory, and that the evidence may help explain certain familiar observations that baffle us now. For example, alcohol is known to be one of the substances that produces radical and permanent changes in proteins. This process, called denaturing, might account for the hallucinations and loss of memory which are symptoms of certain forms of alcoholism.

As a general rule, protein molecules can produce exact copies of themselves, or at least copies that are close enough to the original so that it doesn't make much difference. But occasional flaws may be more serious. They may be the underlying cause of false memories, "recollections" of things that never happened but seem as real as if they had. Although such slip-ups usually concern minor details only, they can add up. To test the accuracy of memory, a college professor once arranged to have his lecture interrupted by a student, acting according to a previously worked-out plan. The student suddenly dashed to the front of the classroom and fired three shots at the professor. Of course, the shots were blanks and the outburst had been carefully rehearsed beforehand. The point became clear when the class was asked to describe what had happened. The students produced a dozen different versions of the mock attacker's words and various conflicting statements about the number of shots fired. No two stories were in complete agreement. A large and profitable part of the legal profession owes its existence to the fact that our testimony is not infallible.

Is snapshot memory a matter of self-duplicating protein molecules? There is no direct proof and all the evidence to date is circumstantial. But we have a strong hunch that we are on the right track. If so, our research would reveal strange relationships among things that would offhand appear to have little in common. The thirty thousand genes which transmit hereditary traits from generation to generation are also self-duplicating proteins. So are the submicroscopic viruses which cause infantile paralysis, smallpox and other diseases. And according to current biological theory, so were the first "living" things on earth. Snapshot memory seems to be linked with such molecules, with the fundamental processes of heredity, disease and the origin of life itself.

The varieties of memory have important qualities in common. For one thing, after a trace has been formed in your brain you are different from what you were before—and the difference persists. The trace produces alterations in structures which are continuously altered by previous traces, so that increasingly complex patterns grow up among our nerve cells. In a sense, each trace represents something pulled out of time, something captured from the flow of events and preserved for future reference. At any given moment we are the sum of all our memories and all the marks they have made upon our nervous systems.

7

MEMORY AND THE HIGHER FACULTIES

Some time ago a little girl was walking through the fields near her home in Canada. She remembers that it was a lovely summer day. Her two brothers were playing together somewhere ahead. She could not see them clearly, because the grass was so high. Suddenly she heard a rustling noise and turned around. A strange man with a bag in his hand had come up behind her. He said: "How would you like to get into this bag with the snakes?" The girl screamed to her brothers, and the children ran home to tell their mother about the experience.

The incident, reinforced by intense feelings of terror, was engraved deeply in the girl's memory. She was seven years old at the time and relived the details in frequent nightmares. Four years later the scene and the stranger began appearing as vivid hallucinations in broad daylight. Convulsions followed and the patient was finally referred to the Montreal Neurological Institute, one of the world's leading medical centers for brain research and the treatment of nervous diseases. All indications pointed to chronic irritation in a localized area on the right side of the cortex.

Removal of the area might end the hallucinations and relieve the convulsions. Dr. Wilder Penfield, director of the Institute, performed the operation successfully. To explore the suspected area before actually operating on the brain, and to check results afterward, he touched various points on the exposed brain with an electrical stimulator. Among other things he found that stimulating a certain point caused the girl to remember her frightening childhood experience. At the first touch of the electrical contact, she started describing things from the very beginning, one incident after the other.

The details came out in their proper order—and they continued to come during the entire period that the contact was held in place. The longer it touched the cortex, the further the story progressed. But as soon as it was removed, the story stopped as abruptly as an announcer's voice stops when you turn off your radio. When the stimulator was placed on the same point once more, the story did not pick up where it left off. It started all over again. These were "forced" memories—that is, the girl did not choose to recall them and could not stop recollecting until stimulation ceased.

WHERE IS MEMORY?

Such observations and many others have directed attention to the so-called temporal lobes of the cortex. The girl's injury and the points Dr. Penfield studied were located in these areas, sheets of gray matter covering the sides of the brain and folding inward beneath its base. The word "temporal" refers to the fact that parts of the regions lie under the temples at the sides of the head. But the name was invented before we knew what we know now, and it represents a kind of unintentional pun. "Temporal" also means "pertaining to time," and the temporal regions are very much concerned with time—time past, as preserved in memory.

A sharp blow on the side of the head may produce characteristic lapses of memory. George Kell, playing third base for the Detroit Tigers, was once struck squarely on the temple by a line drive. He bent over, grabbed the ball, sized up the situation, and threw out his man at third base. Then he collapsed. Afterward in the clubhouse, he had forgotten completing the play and everything else about the accident. Another baseball player was hit on the side of the head by a fast curve when he was at bat, and went on to pitch six shutout innings and win the game. But he remembered nothing about what happened during that period.

An even more dramatic story, reported recently in the *New York Times,* dates back nearly thirty years when Jack Sharkey was a contender for the heavyweight championship. Sharkey was walking past the Yankee Stadium with his manager: "I don't like the looks of that sky. It might rain and I'd hate to have my fight postponded."

"What fight?"

"Are you my manager or aren't you!" Sharkey retorted. "I don't want to surprise you but I'm fighting Jack Dempsey in the Stadium tonight."

"This may be news to you, but you've already fought Dempsey. He knocked you out in the seventh round."

Complete blackouts of past episodes are typical of damage to the temporal lobes of the cortex. When the regions are hurt, no memory traces may be formed. Sharkey knew exactly what he was doing during the fight. He recognized his manager, followed advice and put up a good battle. He was completely conscious and had access to past memories. But his brain was not producing records of current events. In other words, the immediate past was represented by short-term memory only, eddying currents in nerve-cell circuits. The eddies stopped after the knockout. Although the previous memories of the boxer were left intact, there was a gap— a "hole" in his past—for the time of the fighting.

Sharkey's condition is quite different from the form of memory loss which shuts a person off from his past. An amnesia patient may forget his age, his name, his occupation. He does not know where or with whom he lives. But he remembers recent events; he can form new memory traces. Old traces, while probably intact, cannot be reached. There are some flaws of the mechanisms which permit us to search through our memories and select the information we want. A sharp blow on the head may bring about such symptoms or cause them to disappear, as if the jarring effect itself could put things back in running order.

This sort of evidence does not mean that we have at long last located "the seat of memory" or anything remotely resembling it. Brain investigators might have one less major problem to worry over if a compact, anatomically distinct nerve center for memory had been found. But the brain itself would probably work a good deal less efficiently. Memory is far too voluminous and valuable to entrust to any single group of nerve cells. There are probably storage places in lower centers as well as in the cortex, and much information may be filed away in the networks of the brainstem. But the temporal lobes of the cortex seem to play a special part in the making of traces and in evoking them at some later time.

The lobes are also involved in a kind of false memory or false recognition. When this condition occurs, it brings on strange feelings—feelings which most of us experience from time to time. The popular song "Where or When" describes it with clinical accuracy: "Some things that happen for the first time seem to be happening again." Circumstances we have never before lived through arouse a feeling of recognition which wells up in us like a deep emotion. You are sitting in a living room and someone is talking to you. You notice an ashtray on the table near the couch, a cushion, a lamp, a wisp of smoke. Suddenly you feel that you have seen all these things before, arranged in the same patterns in time and space. You also feel that you have already heard what the person talking to you is saying and is about to say—the same words, spoken with the same intonations. For a while an aura of the familiar, of having known it all, hovers about everything.

Experiences of this sort can produce profound effects. At any cocktail party you will find persons who interpret them as flashes of intuition or the release of clairvoyant forces. They have even been cited as proof of Einstein's theory of relativity. The future is not entirely closed to us, just as the past is not entirely accessible. But our unexpected feelings of recognition are not forecasts. Psychologists tell us that they seem to depend on coincidental similarities between past and present experiences. After all, most living rooms are more alike than different. The furnishings of one living room, and the events that go on in it, may resemble those of another so closely that our memories are deceived.

There is another explanation based on more recent studies. Folded up against the underside of the brain is a curved, hook-shaped extension of the temporal lobe, a part of the ancient cortex or smell-brain.

It contains the center which receives nerve impulses from the nose, and some people have feelings of false recognition just after detecting particular odors, usually bad ones. This fact indicates that things are happening in the temporal-lobe region. Injury to the same area may produce the same feelings. More often than not the effects are like a disorder of memory but, basically, it is probably something quite different.

When the "hook" area is damaged, peculiar changes may take place in our interpretation of events, unpleasant and otherwise. The identity of an event may be denied in various ways. For example, one patient who had been knocked unconscious and robbed knew exactly what had happened, but claimed it had not happened to him. (Also, he frequently complained of unpleasant odors.) Other patients say the event only seemed to have occurred. Still others rob the event of its uniqueness—and, indirectly, of some of its shocking qualities—by saying that it had all taken place before. This, the false recognition we have been discussing, is thus only one of many ways of denying some aspect of reality.

It was commonly reported during World War II among soldiers advancing into battle. Later they told doctors that, as they approached closer and closer to danger, everything seemed unreal. They felt as if they had been lifted out of themselves and were spectators watching themselves move forward. They often felt "pepped up," joyous and lighthearted. The situation seemed to have occurred at some previous time. One psychiatrist believes that under such circumstances the men notice a few features of the present scene which remind them of the past and recall events of less dangerous days. Clearly they may have good reason to deny the identity of the present as completely as possible, without failing in their duties as soldiers.

Putting Your Thoughts Together

In the last chapter, and so far in this chapter, we have discussed different types of memory, some parts of the brain which seem to be involved and possible methods of storage. We have pointed out that enduring records of things that were may exist as the coming together of branching nerve fibers, and as "imprints" on self-duplicating protein molecules inside nerve cells. The problem of how the storage process works, how traces are organized, has not yet been considered. In other words, how are our memories filed so that we can use them efficiently? This question cannot be answered definitely on the basis of what we know today. But certain facts hint at the nature of the filing system, and of these, two are particularly significant: (1) the brain can be damaged extensively without seriously affecting our stored memories; and (2) our memory traces can be used to detect general relationships and form abstract ideas.

Memory may survive the destruction of large areas of the brain. This observation is illustrated by a famous case in the archives of brain research—the case of Phineas Gage, foreman at a Vermont stone quarry. The story is told in a pair of medical papers with unusually simple and direct titles: "Passage of an Iron Rod through the Head" published in 1848, and "Recovery from the Passage of an Iron Bar through the Head" published twenty years later. The foreman was using a crowbar to drive a charge of gunpowder into a hole drilled in rock for blasting. Suddenly the charge exploded prematurely. The crowbar shot into his lower left cheek, up through the center of his brain, and protruded from the top of his skull.

Gage recovered from the accident. He returned to work, although not as foreman. According to his doctor's report, he was not fit for responsibility: "He is fitful, irreverent; indulging at times in the grossest profanity (which was not previously his custom), manifesting but little deference for his fellows, impatient of restraint or advice when it conflicts with his desires, at times pertinaciously obstinate, yet capricious and vacillating." In short, his personality had changed radically. But he worked as skillfully as ever, and there was no evidence that his memory had been impaired in any way.

Many studies carried out since then confirm the fact that memory is difficult to destroy. Once you remember something, the odds are that you will not un-remember it. Animal experiments indicate that in certain areas of the cortex which play a role in storing visual impressions more than 90 per cent of the nerve cells can be destroyed without affecting memory at all. During operations for brain tumors surgeons have removed half the brain, an entire hemisphere—and the patients later did excellently in tests calculated to discover how well they could remember and memorize. Of course, these results could be accounted for by assuming that there are duplicate records, one set in each hemisphere, a definite possibility.

But there is more to it than that. Consider snapshot memory. You are driving along a highway and suddenly, up ahead, you see a smashed-up car being pulled off to the side. You drive by, but the scene—snapped through your eyes' cameralike "shutters" in a tenth of a second—is retained in your memory. It is not stored in one place, or in one piece. The scene is stored as a pattern of individual traces, producing lasting changes in protein molecules. Each molecule is like one of the silver grains imbedded in the emulsion of a photographic plate, bearing its own fraction of the total picture. Your memory of the smashed car on the parkway consists of a mosaic of imprints on up to a thousand protein molecules.

The mosaic is not believed to be a compact one, in that it is located in a tiny part of the brain. Its "pieces" are probably scattered in many nerve cells forming a three-dimensional pattern, a kind of memory-constellation in space. Such an arrangement might help explain why memory is preserved after many cells have been destroyed. In a mosaic originally built up of a thousand pieces, you can recognize the picture even though a good many pieces are missing. In other words, by scattering memory traces the brain insures its records of times past. Generals follow the same policy when they order their troops to disperse during an enemy artillery bombardment or air raid.

As pointed out previously, you will take about ten billion snapshots during your lifetime. Every snapshot, every individual memory, is broken into bits or traces and stored in the impressionable molecules of hundreds of cells. The total experience is dissected, and each part is dissected again and again down to the finest unit. Objects and scenes are composites of color, smell, shape, size, texture and a legion of other details. Ideas have far more subtle characteristics. Your brain dissects and disperses them all, everything from apples and faces to political opinions and religious beliefs.

Behind such activities are cerebral mechanisms so complicated that we have little notion of their actual nature. But the problem of preserving and insuring memory is simple compared to that of using the traces to form abstract ideas. In fact, how we make anything of our traces is one of the great mysteries of brain research. From the millions upon millions of mosaic-patterns of traces tucked away in your head, you can at a moment's notice reassemble that particular set of traces which forms a particular scene. Years later you can reconstruct an image of the smashed car in your "mind's eye."

Not only that, but by uttering certain sounds or putting marks on paper you can make other people reassemble their memory traces and produce in their head rough replicas of the wreck you saw long ago. Upon seeing another wreck you can check its features against those of the former wreck and re-cognize, or know again, various details. You may also imagine, create images of unicorns and mermaids and Edens and other never-seen things. Apparently you can play with the pieces of memory's mosaics. They seem to be universal parts, atoms of experience that can be put together in an enormous number of ways to form new images and new ideas.

These are some of the remarkable feats we accomplish with our memory traces. But our ability to conceive and deal with abstractions, to make generalities, represents perhaps the most remarkable of the brain's powers. The brain does such things because of the very nature of its design. It is built to do them. It surveys a set of stored items and detects an element or feature common to the whole lot. It abstracts, or separates an underlying similarity from a large number of experiences which are dissimilar in many obvious ways.

The game of making abstractions goes on much of the time. What do the following things have in common: the moon, a tree trunk, a wheel, a coin, a clock? A good education may help a child to answer that all five objects have a circular form, and to notice more subtle relationships as he grows older. But the important fact to remember is that there is something about the construction of the brain itself, the workings and patterns of its nerve cells, which almost forces us to think in this way—or at least appreciably increases the probability that we will detect general similarities.

Again, we do not know how this is done. But it obviously requires an efficient and reliable filing system. Yesterday your brain took and stored more than half a million snapshots of the world. It is taking and storing about the same number today, and it will continue doing so tomorrow and tomorrow and tomorrow. The brain files the snapshots and keeps special track of those features which are most important to it. In other words, each snapshot is somehow cross-indexed under many different subject headings, perhaps thirty or more. And somehow, when the occasion arises, we can extract the common property of redness or squareness or threeness from groups of objects.

Incidentally, we can extract common qualities from different actions as well as from different objects. The British psychiatrist W. Ross Ashby points out that even the simplest actions may be built up out of basic movements of the muscles, movements "abstracted" from more complex actions which were learned long ago. For example, putting the cap back on a fountain pen involves the elements of movements previously developed for such purposes as putting a finger into the mouth or through the handle of a cup, buttoning a shirt and lacing a shoe. We have been discussing stored memories, but the word "stored" may be too tame. The brain is a dynamic system of cells. It never stops using and reusing its memory traces, adding new items, or trying new combinations. The abstractions it makes are used, among other things, to help us predict.

Things to Come

Then the great empire of Antichrist will begin in the Arda and Zerfus, to descend in great and innumerable numbers, so that with the coming of the Holy Spirit, proceeding from the Twenty-fourth degree, shall make the transmigration, chasing out the abomination of the Antichrist who made war against the royal one, who will be the great Vicar of Jesus Christ; and against His Church and reign for a time and to the end of time.

Thunderstorms, highest in the upper 80's. Tides: High—1:30 A.M., 2:12 P.M. Low—8:03 A.M., 8:10 P.M.
Sunrise—5:03 A.M. Sunset—8:25 P.M.

The first of these forecasts, made four hundred years ago by Nostradamus, is supposed to describe Hitler's defeat. The second is self-explanatory. Whatever you may think of the French prophet or the weather man (and there are strong opinions about both), certain differences stand out between the predictions of the sixteenth and twentieth centuries. As a rule, we narrow the scope of our forecasts. We have sacrificed grandeur for brevity, precision and clarity. We go less by revelation and more by observation.

But one element has not changed. Seers have always searched the past for clues to the future. Memory is the storehouse of all our traditions, of all the things we admire most and strive to emulate. Yet it does not exist primarily to serve times past, certainly not to glorify or regret them. Chronic nostalgia is one of its diseases. In extreme cases the symptoms are living in the good old days, awe for the wisdom of dead people and dead institutions, contempt for today's ideas and discoveries. Memory, our record of the past, exists above all to serve and shape the future.

In an important sense, we are predicting every instant of our lives. It has been said that the past is that about which you may know a little but cannot alter; the future is that about which you may do a little but cannot know. If so, the present is that about which you can neither know nor do anything. We are always living a bit in the past, because of the delay between sensation and action. For the brain there is no present. You suddenly see a red light and decide to stop your car. At best it takes you about three quarters of a second to jam on the brakes; on the average, it may take a full second or more.

Such delays are not too important in daily living, but during emergencies they may make the difference between life and death. They are so important when it comes to piloting jet planes at seven hundred miles an hour that many controls are handled by electronic machines. But whatever the delay, you can never quite catch up with the present, the "now" of the world. For varying periods you are forced to act "blind," to act as if what was will continue to be. When you are blinded by the headlights of an oncoming car, you predict that the road will continue to curve in the way it started to curve before the glare—and you steer accordingly.

This is how we cope with all coming events. Our expectations may extend further into the future. The more we know beforehand, the more successful we are likely to be. But we are always driving in the dark on winding roads. It is always a gamble, for better or for worse, until death do us part. Every now and then the future refuses to come out as it "should," and we learn. Then we carry our new ideas about the past over into the future again, and act on that basis until we are again mistaken. We usually become wiser as we accumulate experience. Predicting is one of the most spectacular things the brain does with memory traces, and sooner or later brain research will have to come to grips with the problem of how it works.

Lower animals also predict. Watch a sea gull circling high above the water and scanning the surface for signs of fish. When it sees a fish, it hovers an instant and then dives like a released bomb. The dive is aimed, not at the fish's present position, but at some other position where the sea gull expects its prey to be by the time it hits the water. The sea gull takes the direction and velocity of the wind into account, as well as the probable escape tactics of various fish. Its forecasts are sufficiently accurate to keep its stomach full.

Prediction evolved during relentless pursuits and desperate efforts to get away. It developed as animals became faster and more deadly, as the brain advanced from a tiny bulge of cells and tangled fibers to a massive control organ. The hunter coming in for the kill anticipated the dodgings of the hunted. The hunted, in turn, learned to anticipate the moves of the hunter—and to try new dodges. The game was played for the highest stakes. For the individual, losing meant death; for the species, it meant extinction. With the increasingly complex interplay of offensive and defensive tactics the future became less of a mystery.

Our games are somewhat less bloodthirsty, at least during peacetime. But the general principles are the same. The evolution of a star halfback, for example, indicates how our predicting abilities are developed and refined. First comes increasing experience, the accumulating memories of what hundreds of tacklers and would-be tacklers did. There are recollections of many losses and short gains, and a few touchdown runs. To every recollection are attached a mass of details about what happened during each stage of the play, the emotions that went with it and the remarks of the football coach. Memory is busy making its traces and putting them in its store-houses.

Meanwhile a significant process is taking place. The budding halfback begins to realize that certain situations which came up again and again have certain things in common. His brain is begin-ning to classify its memory traces. Many of the traces are unim-portant, representing such details as the appearance of the opposing players or the color of their uniforms. These are not used. But the traces which represent running and dodging tactics are sorted out and compared. Significant similarities are discovered among them and become a guide for future action. New patterns are being built out of traces selected from many memories. To predict, the brain must have tally sheets of some sort. In this case, it lists all attempted maneuvers by the degree of their success or failure.

Like a gambler, it figures out the odds and refuses to "bet" on tactics that rarely pay off in terms of yardage gained. It selects those tactics which offer the highest probability of success. The halfback learns that a fast, two-stage maneuver—say, a feint to the left and a dash to the right—is sufficient to avoid a large proportion of tacklers. For special emergencies he may be skillful enough to use a three-stage maneuver, feinting to the left, feinting to the right and then running to the left (a runner seldom has time for more involved tactics). An authority on the subject, Dick Kazmaier, Princeton's All-American back of several years ago, summed it up: "Play patterns repeat and the stored-up experiences enable me to know what's going to happen. The big difference comes from repetitious situa-tions."

Repeating events are the raw material for all prediction. Of course, nature usually stops us with subtle riddles rather than any-thing as crude as a tackle. An astronomer, like a halfback, studies the actions of his "opponents." Stars and planets still frustrate him by their antics, although he has solved a large number of baffling problems. We need his experience in navigating ships and airplanes and in controlling certain types of guided missiles. Someday we may be launching interplanetary rockets, which means avoiding many moving bodies en route as well as landing on our targets. We are continually probing the future of stars, atoms, people. We are learning to forecast more things further in advance.

Prediction is a kind of sense which reduces our chances of being caught napping by the unexpected. It prevents us from being surprised quite so often. To refine and extend our forecasts we have developed ways of assisting the brain—or the brain has developed ways of assisting itself. Words are condensed memories, shorthand for patterns of memory traces. We use them to aid thinking and help make new patterns. But if words stand for vast amounts of information, mathematical symbols compress whole universes of experience into compact markings on paper. Mathematical symbols are shorthand for many words, and some of them would require volumes to translate into familiar sentences. Without them we would know far less than we do about the future.

The brain also needs business machines, computers and other devices to help it make predictions. Forecasting elections, for example, is a hazardous profession even if we forget what happened in 1948. It takes machines to increase the accuracy of long-range weather forecasts, analyze the supply problems of our armies and predict the nation's industrial and population trends. Politics and social change move faster and are more complex than the thinking processes of the unaided brain. Perhaps machines of the future will help us catch up.

INFLUENCING PEOPLE

Intelligence involves everything from sensation to prediction, and many factors we may not yet be aware of. It has reached a peak in us, partly because we have twice as many nerve cells as the highest ape. That means more room for memory traces and more opportunity for creating new patterns. Doubling the number of cells makes a tremendous difference. There are 635,013,559,600 possible bridge hands. But if you double the number of cards, the total of thirteen-card patterns becomes about twenty thousand times greater. This may give you some indication of the number of new patterns made possible by increasing the cells in the brain from twenty-five to fifty billion. Your position on the I.Q. scale depends on your ability to create such patterns from your memory traces.

Creating patterns takes little energy. Half a salted peanut provides sufficient calories for an hour of intense mental effort. We use most of our food to translate thoughts into action. But first the brain alerts the muscles. We not only know what we are going to do before we do it. We are ready to behave in a very definite way. A pianist is prepared to execute a long and elaborate series of motions. He may strike more than a hundred keys a second, and each step of his performance has been mapped out ahead of time, down to the contraction of his smallest muscle. Furthermore, the steps are arranged so that they follow one another in the proper order. The result is a super-pattern, a thing of patterns within patterns.

Many common mistakes can be traced to mix-ups in our prearranged sequences. An outfielder may be so anxious to complete a play that he starts to throw the ball before he catches it, and another error is entered in the record books. Typing errors are often of a similar nature. So are slips of speech, particularly the sort known as spoonerisms. W. A. Spooner, an Oxford don who probably suffered from a minor brain defect, was famous for statements such as "Don't you ever feel a half-warmed fish?" (instead of "half-formed wish") and "our queer old dean" (instead of "our dear old queen"). All these mistakes involve variations on the theme of putting the horse behind the cart.

As a rule, however, we follow our schedules to the letter. Just before we act a kind of nerve-muscle tension is built up which may be related to what we call determination or will power. The brain prepares us to go places and do things. Where we go and what we do are something else again. These are largely a matter of interacting brains, clashing ideas and ideals, and systems competing for the allegiance of the individual. Those concerned with the art of

influencing people have developed many techniques to attain
their ends. The list includes diplomacy, sermons, jingles and the
broadcasts that go with them, and other forms of persuasion. In
all cases the general aim is the same—to create or reinforce patterns in many brains at once.

As a target for such tactics, the brain has certain advantages and
certain drawbacks. It can be influenced, particularly during the
early years of life. In fact, it is constructed specifically to be influenced. The gray mantle of the cortex is like a mansion with thousands of miles of extension wires and a near-infinity of wall outlets.
The wires have octopus plugs, and new connections are being made
to form an electrical network of steadily increasing complexity.
The versatility of the brain is such that we can do or believe almost
anything. The circus acrobat sitting on a chair balanced by two
legs on a high tight-wire (and no net below) performs out in the
open for all to see and applaud. Less obvious but just as real are
some of the dreams and ambitions we hold precariously during
peace and war.

Innumerable associations are possible for us. We can attach hate
or love or disgust or any one of our feelings to anything—beer,
deodorants, soap, family, nation, world. Advertising agencies and
public-relations firms specialize in establishing reputations and
causes, and have evolved the methods of influencing people to the
finest point. Their job is to see to it that we use our memory traces
to form the patterns selected by their clients. If necessary, and if
the price is right, they guarantee to provide any traces we may lack.

The catch to all such activities is that the brain is too receptive.
It takes in many things, because that is what it is designed to do.
Tramps as well as honored guests are certain to find room and lodg-
ing. The brain cannot help storing memory traces and rear-
ranging them into new patterns. Propagandists can furnish a few
traces and even determine minor features of the patterns. But they
cannot get inside; they have no way of boring from within. History
is a record of unsuccessful efforts to isolate people behind stone
walls and other forerunners of today's iron curtains. Inevitably,

other people with other ideas come in and learning proceeds as before.

We must learn, just as we must breathe. Death is the only thing that can stop either process—and then for the individual only. The species does not stop learning. We sometimes regret the changes that come with learning, but it is the loss of our ability to change that ultimately kills us. A little-used brain is withering as surely as a little-used muscle. Research is under way on new ways of keeping us learning after our school years. There is also research on new ways of feeding us dogmas. The brain, by the very flexibility of its organization, is on the side of the angels.

Meanwhile we continue to be centers of continually changing patterns. Many conflicting forces act upon us at once. Some would excite, others depress us. The net effect of many tuggings, pluses and minuses, is the way we feel and behave. Analysis is often helpful, because it permits us to focus on one or a few things at a time. But many of our experiences have too many factors, and in the end we throw our analyses back into the pool of feeling and proceed "intuitively." Intuition is like the behavior of a compass needle which, immersed in a vast and intricate magnetic field of unknown origin, simply points. Our intuitions are extremely simple responses to situations too complex to analyze and too pressing to ignore. Until we know a great deal more than we know now they will continue to guide us in love, politics and war.

8

CELLS IN RHYTHM

A NURSE was pasting a small metal strip to the patient's scalp, right over his right temple. As I watched, fifteen more strips were set in place, one over the other temple and the others at selected locations on the top and back of his head. Colored wires led from the strips to a dial-studded machine about the size of an office desk. A switch was flipped to the "ON" position, and eight automatic pens began scratching away on a moving ribbon of graph paper.

The metal strips were electrodes, electrical contacts designed to pick up signals being produced in the patient's brain. After about twenty minutes, the machine completed its paperwork and was turned off. The nurse removed a neatly folded chart more than a hundred feet long from it. This was an electroencephalogram—literally, a record of electricity inside the head, or "EEG" for short. It consisted of jagged inked lines, resembling a long series of illegible signatures. But after examining thousands of such brain-wave records and recognizing patterns that come up again and again, investigators have learned to make out some of the signatures. In this case, the patterns confirmed a suspected diagnosis.

A doctor picked up the chart and started to examine it, a foot or so at a time, as if he were following stock-market trends on a ticker tape. "We think this man has a brain tumor. . . . The record looks all right here. Those are normal waves. . . . He works in a television studio, an executive or something, headaches and speech difficulties. . . . Nothing much here, either. . . . He gets worse when he's under emotional pressure, can't talk. . . . There. See those large slow waves? They come from the left temporal region, the left side of the brain. . . . That's where the trouble is." The trouble turned out to be a quarter-sized tumor which was removed successfully a week later.

Electrical records do not always indicate the presence of diseases in the brain. Even when they do, it may not be possible to locate the source of the disturbance. On the other hand, they may furnish an important and sometimes the only clue to the nature and extent that would otherwise be inaccessible to us, messages intended for internal circulation only. We have learned to intercept many of the messages produced by sick nerve cells. But we could never interpret our records unless we had some idea of how intact cells behave, some standard of comparison to help us distinguish health from disease. The use of EEG tests in medicine depends on continuing studies of normal brains—however difficult it may be to decide what is normal and what is not.

LIVING BATTERIES

Nerve cells are electrical signaling devices like telegraph relays or the blinking searchlights of a battleship. Each cell is equipped with a built-in storage battery that supplies the energy needed for its messages. It gathers quantities of electricity and holds them ready for instant release upon demand. When it is stimulated, it discharges and automatically recharges itself in a thousandth of a second. But it need not simply sit and wait. Telegraph keys will not click unless they are tapped or receive electrical impulses. Nerve cells are more independent. Under the proper conditions they can act on their own.

A cell may start charging and discharging at fairly regular intervals, flashing on and off in a kind of electrical "beat." For a time it may flash alone in a region of hundreds of thousands of cells, a lighthouse isolated in a cerebral sea. But nerve cells are communal creatures and soon the rhythm spreads. First a few near-by cells take up the beat, although they may improvise a bit and may not be in perfect time. Then cells more and more remote from the original pace-setter are affected, as the rhythm gradually builds up to a high pitch of nervous activity. Finally, whole populations of cells get into the swing of things.

The same sort of process goes on at any large-scale demonstration or political rally. Suddenly, and for reasons that are not always evident, some member of the audience takes it into his head to start clapping. Other people promptly follow along. They clap in their own fashion and with varying degrees of enthusiasm, so that at first the effect is scattered and irregular. But by the time everyone has joined in, individual differences can no longer be heard. Individual rhythms merge into a single dominating rhythm of applause. Brain waves are the applause of millions of nerve cells pulsing together. The "clapping" may produce inked deflections on the EEG tape.

EEG patterns change from birth on. An infant is a mass of unshaped and unco-ordinated activities, haphazard jerks and squirmings, experimental gropings. Its brain waves are not so organized as they will be later on. Like specialists in bebop and more eccentric varieties of modern jazz, they produce more off-beats than anything else. The record of a newborn infant is a jumble of lines as chaotic as the average doodle. It represents the charging and discharging of cells that have not yet learned to act in unison. There are few waves, and the ones that can be observed flare up and die down spasmodically.

This is the almost meaningless baby-talk of immature nerve cells. But the brain begins to talk sense early in life. Brain waves acquire shape and rhythm with advancing years and form distinctive patterns as we learn to control our behavior and take our places in society. Rhythms make their debut at the age of one month. They can be detected by placing electrodes over the back of the head, over the visual areas of the cortex. At this age the infant is just beginning to give the world a visual once-over and size up the situation before doing something about it. It focuses one inquisitive eye on objects around its crib (binocular focusing doesn't come for another month or so).

The first rhythms are produced by nerve cells flashing together at a rate of about three electrical pulses per second. They are slow waves, relatively high from trough to crest. Soon their pace quickens. An accelerating cerebral drumbeat heralds the ripening of the brain. A rhythm of four to seven pulses per second is a characteristic feature of the EEG until the eighth year, the "age of reason" when Catholic children are considered ready to study the last part of the catechism and the growth curve of the cortex is reaching a peak. Then ten-per-second waves begin to take over—and remain prominent throughout adult life. These are the so-called alpha waves.

The dominating rhythm is easy to recognize after seeing a few EEG charts. It writes its signature as a series of fine ripples and has been called a "wave of inattention" because, as pointed out previously, it appears when you relax and are not concentrating on anything in particular. Your mind wanders with a rhythm of ten pulses per second as it idly scans its own contents and those of the world outside. The instant the brainstem alerts the cortex and you focus your attention, however, the waves are blocked and fade or vanish entirely. The ripples on the chart flatten out when you watch a television broadcast, hear a loud noise, figure out your income tax or become emotionally upset.

At least this is what happens when most of us pay attention. But it does not happen in all cases. In fact, any time you come across the word "all" in a statement about the way our brains perform, you had better be on your guard. The odds are that it's all wrong. Some perfectly healthy people have unusual, not abnormal, alpha waves that are extremely difficult to block even during intense concentration. Others hardly show this sort of wave at all, even when they close their eyes and keep their minds blank. Missouri-born Dr. W. Grey Walter of the Burden Neurological Institute in Bristol, England, is an authority on brain waves. He has made special studies of these exceptions to the rule and believes he has discovered some important relationships between personality and brain rhythms.

What goes on in your mind when you think of "The Star-Spangled Banner"? Most people experience a wide variety of impressions. But many of us recall in interesting and unusual ways. Do you think in Technicolor? Do you see the flag in red, white and blue, bombs bursting with flashes of red fire, the green grass of a baseball diamond and white-shirted fans singing the national anthem? If you think almost exclusively in terms of vivid, colorful images—whether it is a song, a story, next week's business trip, an argument about free will, or the Lord's Prayer—the nerve cells in your brain probably do not produce strong alpha rhythms. You probably have an "M" or "minus" type of brain-wave record. But if you do very little visualizing, if you specialize in recalling sounds and movements and the way things feel, you are likely to have "P" or "persistent" alpha rhythms (that is, ten-per-second waves which do not block out readily).

Persons with M and P records make up an appreciable part of the total population, perhaps more than 30 per cent. This is an unfortunate state of affairs. The two types not only think differently as a rule—they tend to get along atrociously with one another. Dr. Walter happens to be an extreme M type, with hardly any alpha waves at all. He also makes many friends, and is generous in sharing his time and information. But some years ago he and a laboratory worker formed a particularly intense aversion for each other's company. The colleague's brain waves were recorded and interpreted, not by Dr. Walter himself who might well have been prejudiced but by a neutral colleague. They definitely belonged to the P category.

Since then further studies show that when M and P type persons meet, innocent by-standers had better run for cover. Their arguments are usually bitter, intense and settle nothing. This doesn't mean that you can now blame your brain waves, or the other person's for life's brief and unpleasant encounters. Neither you nor your enemies may have unusual records, and you probably have sound reasons for most of your quarrels. But brain waves may be clues to personality differences that produce more irrational dislikes. Two people meeting for the first time may instinctively distrust one another, exchange a few remarks and part with permanently ruffled feelings. The Bristol group is expanding its research to learn what, if anything, its findings have to do with personal and social relations in general.

Other unusual rhythms have been found among people who are not suffering from any recognized form of brain disease. For example, eight young Communists aged sixteen to eighteen once visited Dr. Walter's laboratory and were promptly given brain-wave tests. Six of the group showed exceptionally prominent rhythms of four to seven pulses per second—the sort that generally disappear around the age of ten. Such results, however, do not provide us with a new test for subversive activity. "Observation of other groups suggest that these rhythms are not characteristic of communism only or of youth only," Dr. Walter explains, "but rather of extremely emotional views of any color, even when not attached to any organized policy or religion."

CLEVER HANS

Doctors take such out-of-the-ordinary patterns into account when they test patients. But generally the things they look for produce distinctive rhythms, and EEG records are being used on an increasing scale. This trend is based mainly on research conducted within the last twenty years. The man who discovered human brain waves, Dr. Hans Berger of the University of Jena in Germany, published his first paper in 1929. He used standard radio equipment to detect the waves produced by pulsing nerve cells, and amplified their weak signals more than a million times.

Dr. Berger's original paper received little notice and most of that was unfavorable. It appeared at a bad time as far as getting recognition was concerned. The world was far more interested in the theories of Freud. Psychoanalysis was entering its heyday period and influencing more and more psychiatrists in Europe and the United States. Dreams were being interpreted in a new way; new words had been coined to describe the revelations of the unconscious. These ideas attracted artists and writers as well as physicians.

Electricity could no more compete with sex in those days than it can now.

Dr. Berger seemed slightly ridiculous to many of his contemporaries. They thought in terms of the ego, the superego, the id, Oedipus complexes. He thought in terms of EEG charts, voltages and other equally undramatic things. They found guilt and wish-fulfillment in the mind. Using crude vacuum-tube devices, he found electricity in the brain. He provided his subjects with beer and dull books when he wanted to put them to sleep and take records of the dreaming brain. To study the effects of emotion on the brain waves, he once exploded a firecracker near an unsuspecting volunteer and calmly noted when the ten-per-second alpha rhythms disappeared and reappeared.

All this was obviously out of step with the research fashion of the times—and in medicine, as in other fields, being out of step can often be unpleasant. Psychoanalysts who not long ago had been derided for their own ideas, were just as merciless when it came to the matter of Dr. Berger and his brain waves. They invented a special nickname for the German professor, a nickname that persons not in the know might have interpreted as a compliment. They called him *"der kluge Hans,"* German for "clever Hans." But it happened that this was also the name of a popular horse which had been performing before large vaudeville audiences and tapped out answers to simple questions with an educated right hoof. Dr. Berger retaliated by prohibiting the teaching of psychoanalysis in his hospital.

"Clever Hans" did nothing to win over the sympathies of either skeptics or neutrals. He was not a warm person and made few friends. He walked with the bearing of a Prussian officer and ran his hospital accordingly. One of his colleagues during the early days described the beginning of a typical day: "At nine o'clock on the dot Berger entered . . . with quick, brusque steps and grim face. Without looking at anybody he went directly to his place at the head of the table. We were then permitted to sit down." He was aloof and close-lipped, keeping his research secret for years, even from his closest associates. He remained a loyal German citizen until his death.

Research is not customarily judged by the researcher's ability to win friends and influence people. If it were, Dr. Berger's work might still be a subject for heated debates. British investigators checked his findings in 1934 and brain waves were gradually accepted as one of the facts of life. Within five years patients were being tested in special laboratories. It took a bit longer before EEG machines and their custodians were permitted to come out in the open and actually enter the operating room. Records from the exposed brain provided information that cannot be obtained from outside the skull. For example, they may indicate the site of a buried tumor more precisely.

Many surgeons conceded the existence of brain waves. But they were not convinced that the rhythms could help locate tumors or serve any other practical purpose. One surgeon took a quick look at a machine that had been smuggled into his operating room and roared: "Either that damned gadget goes or I go!" The gadget went.

Today such equipment has successfully invaded the operating room along with motion-picture and television cameras. There are about 150 EEG laboratories in the United States and probably as many more in other nations. At one institution alone, the Presbyterian Medical Center in New York, some forty thousand records have been taken during the past decade, which represent more than nine hundred miles of chart paper. Furthermore, half a dozen machines are reeling out more charts at a stepped-up pace of three to four miles a week. EEG tapes are piling up so rapidly that many hospital officials do not know where to put them.

The new machines are far more sensitive than Dr. Berger's early models. In fact, they are so sensitive that they have been known to pick up broadcasts originating from sources outside the brain. Some time ago investigators at the Massachusetts General Hospital in Boston hooked up a loudspeaker to one machine for a special demonstration (brain waves can be recorded in the form of audible beats as well as wavy lines). Electrodes were fastened to the head of a laboratory technician. After all dials had been adjusted to the proper settings, the machine was turned on. At first the loudspeaker emitted a low hum. Then came a bit of static, a sharp click, and something that was definitely not the sound of pulsing nerve cells. "Calling car No. 89! Calling car No. 89! Can you hear me? Over." The investigators had tuned in on the short-wave channel of a local taxicab company. On other occasions the brain's broadcasts have been jammed by police calls, ship-to-shore signals, and the Democratic National Convention. In Chicago during the war interference was traced to radar apparatus scanning Lake Michigan from Navy Pier. EEG machines must be carefully shielded to pick up the messages of the nervous system, and nothing else.

TROUBLEMAKERS

Sick, dying nerve cells still charge and discharge together, but their pulses may be few and far between. Cells squeezed by a growing tumor and deprived of their regular blood supply produce slow rhythms, like those detected in the brain of the television executive with speech difficulties. EEG records are used routinely to find the source of the rhythm and the size of the tumor. They are also used to find abnormally functioning areas in epilepsy. Most patients tested are suffering from one of these two conditions. Other brain-wave research, research that has received little publicity, points toward new discoveries. For one thing, it hints that injured nerve cells may be involved in a condition not usually associated with brain disease—juvenile delinquency.

Important work has been done at a unique institution, the Bradley Home in Providence, R. I. This leading psychiatric hospital for children is located on a gently sloping hill, overlooking Narragansett Bay. The great majority of its patients are classified as victims of behavior disorders. These include the cases who may eventually represent raw material for future crime waves, the movies' dead-end kids and the "bad" children of our reform schools. They come from all over the country and have often been in trouble with school and police authorities in their home towns. Many of them are restless when they enter the Rhode Island hospital, restless to a degree hardly conceivable to most parents.

According to Dr. Maurice Laufer, director of the hospital: "These children are far more active than normal children. The difference is like that between normal children and adults. They seem to climb up the walls. They won't even sit still to look at television!" I saw one newcomer eating breakfast, a nine-year-old boy who had gotten into violent fights with classmates and his younger brothers. He dropped a fork, scrambled under the table after it, bolted across the room to shout at one of the doctors, sat down banging the plate with his elbow, ran after another child, was brought back—all in a few moments. He buzzed about like a chased housefly, and kept it up all day and late into the evening. It reminded me of the animals I had seen with brainstem injuries, animals which walked and could not stop walking until they dropped in their tracks.

There are special "therapy" rooms with chairs, tables, neatly made beds and plenty of toys. Here these children are allowed to release their destructive urges and, in the presence of a sympathetic adult, they may smash practically everything in sight. Another room has a child's painting outside the door, two fire engines and a flaming EEG machine. Bradley investigators have pioneered in brain-wave studies of problem children. Most restless patients have abnormal records with slow rhythms, irregular alpha waves and other peculiar patterns. Dr. Laufer calls them "cerebrally damaged children." They are regularly and successfully treated with benzedrine or a related drug. The surprising thing is that this drug works as a stimulant on normal children and adults, and during the war it was used as a "pep pill" to keep pilots and tank crews awake and alert.

But two tablets taken early in the morning can calm abnormally restless children for the rest of the day. The case of Danny, an aggressive ten-year-old, is typical. Before treatment, he talked and fidgeted incessantly and failed all his courses at private school. After treatment, he quieted down and obtained excellent marks. The only lapse came one morning when his mother overslept and, in the rush of preparing breakfast, forgot to give him his pills. Later that morning she received a telephone call from school. The teacher didn't know what had come over Danny. He'd been behaving so well recently, but today he was out of control again. Dr. Laufer, who has treated more than four hundred children, recalls several other cases where symptoms suddenly reappeared after a daily dose was skipped.

Of course, the drug is by no means the whole treatment. The children have been sick for a long while. They have tried to behave many times and failed many times, even when they knew it meant they would be taken away from home. Such frustration can hurt a healthy child. Children with injured brains are much more sensitive to the impacts of repeated failure, and psychological treatments of all sorts are needed to restore their self-confidence. Furthermore, some parents need a psychiatrist's care more than their children. But under reasonably favorable conditions benzedrine tones down the nervous system as neatly as if you had adjusted a volume-control knob somewhere in the brain. It keeps the restless child out of serious mischief and permits his brain to recover with a minimum of mental conflict. The brain may heal slowly. Often EEG records do not become normal until the patient is fifteen to twenty years old. Then drug treatments stop and, if parents and society have not ruined him emotionally, he will become a well-adjusted citizen.

During Victorian times it was fashionable to muse about the notion that there is no such thing as a "really bad" child. There are only unfortunate children without happy homes to grow up in, little Oliver Twists who behave nicely when they are among nice people. Today, we know that this simple and sentimental hypothesis is not entirely accurate. In many cases the emotional turmoil of unhappy homes may harm a child whose brain was perfectly healthy. But as often as not the brain was probably vulnerable to begin with. Special EEG tests indicate that 40 to 50 per cent of the children coming to the Bradley Home have abnormal brain function resulting from nerve cells that are not working properly.

These facts, discovered at the Providence hospital, have been confirmed at other medical centers in the United States and abroad. In studies of British delinquent children, Dr. Walter found unusual EEG records in about 70 per cent of the group. Prominent in the records were waves similar to those produced by known brain damage—and to those frequently found in infants and during sleep.

Brain-wave studies are arousing an increased interest in problem children with brain disorders, and in possible causes of the damage. Some cases probably inherit bad genes from their parents. Others are victims of birth injuries, like many children suffering from cerebral palsy.

In the next chapter we describe one cerebral sufferer—a seven-year-old boy whose condition was improved by brain surgery. The boy had also been a problem child, destroying property and frequently getting into fights at school and home. The operation affected these symptoms as well as the abnormal movements of his limbs, changing his behavior so that he was happy, co-operative, and well-behaved. Microbes may be another cause of behavior disorders in children. Viruses that direct their attacks against nerve cells are responsible for epidemics of infantile paralysis and sleeping sickness or encephalitis (inflammation of the brain), and both these diseases have produced typical "juvenile delinquents."

Early in August, 1938, an epidemic of encephalitis broke out among horses in southeastern Massachusetts, and three weeks later the malady spread to human beings. The list of Boston patients included a ten-year-old boy, a model child with an I.Q. of 145. He continued to be well-behaved and obtained his usual good marks until more than a year after passing through the crisis of the disease, when he began getting restless and noisy. He struck his mother, gouged holes in the walls with his pocket knife and had screaming temper tantrums followed by fits of remorse. In his case there was no question about the most likely cause. The boy's symptoms were brought under control with benzedrine and have not flared up again.

Is there a special connection between encephalitis, juvenile delinquency and crime? Several years ago a prominent psychiatrist made headlines by answering this question with a definite affirmative. He asserted that an epidemic during the 1920's accounted for the crime wave which struck the nation a decade or so later and claimed that John Dillinger, Public Enemy No. 1 at the time, was a victim of the disease. Although his facts were straight—there was an epidemic and it was followed by a crime wave—few psychiatrists would agree with the implication that a virus-free world would not be plagued by gangsters. Neither viruses nor other invisible things can be made to bear the full burden of our sins.

But crime and brain damage, whether due to encephalitis or other causes, often go together. The most recent evidence comes from a new survey just completed at Maudsley Hospital in London, a survey based on brain-wave research. This is the most extensive EEG study ever made of murderers. In all, 105 killers were tested and half of them had abnormal electrical records. The proportion was even higher among men who had obscure motives for their crimes or no motives at all. For example, one prisoner had killed a friend and her child in the presence of his wife. His only explanation: "I thought what an evil woman she was. . . . I heard the baby crying in the other room and thought the child won't be any good without the mother." London investigators found abnormal rhythms in three out of four such murderers.

New Directions

Unfortunately no unique wave pattern exists for murderers, no EEG signature which we could use to detect potential killers. Helping children who are suffering from behavior disorders is still the most effective way of preventing crime. But the study of brain waves has demonstrated that injured nerve cells are involved far more frequently than was once suspected, and has spurred the search for new and improved medical treatments. It is also changing our basic ideas about crime and punishment—and about mental health in general. When a person limps, we know he has been injured in some way. When a person "limps" mentally, when he thinks or emotes strangely, we rarely consider injury as a reason for his behavior. He simply can't be trusted, he is immoral, repressed or insane. We speak about mental health, but never about the health of the brain.

Are you concerned about your stomach? If so, you can get plenty of advice and some of it may even be good. There are definite things to do, definite diets to be followed and definite medicines to be taken at definite times. Whole libraries of books have been published telling us how to take care of our hearts, teeth, feet, hair, skin. How are we supposed to take care of our brains? We know that worrying isn't good for us, but beyond that most of what we hear adds up to "don't worry" or "try to forget it, chum." (In times like these we should at least have more books telling us how to worry efficiently.)

The lack of practical advice about brain hygiene is one sign of how much we have to learn. But certain recent developments in medical check-ups for prize fighters hint at things to come. For example, a special investigation is under way in Los Angeles and the brain waves of more than 250 boxers have already been studied. These men are not punch-drunk. Most of them fight regularly— say, about a dozen bouts a year—and the idea is to screen out those whose brains may be vulnerable to future injury. Preliminary results reveal that between 30 and 40 per cent of "healthy" prize fighters probably have abnormal rhythms. Also, as you would expect, the more frequently a boxer is knocked down the worse his EEG record becomes.

This doesn't mean that all such boxers will become punch-drunk, or that all boxers with normal records are perfectly safe. But doctors do not go against the odds, and state athletic commissions are beginning to lean heavily on brain-wave evidence. A boxer who wants to fight in New York must first pass an EEG test and, if he is knocked down or severely battered, he'll have to pass another before he can fight again. Some doctors believe there should be stricter laws and more of them. They recommend that all boxers receive regular tests—and that a man with an abnormal record should stay out of the ring until his brain heals sufficiently to generate healthy waves (improvement is sometimes noted after three to six months).

University of Wisconsin investigators have pioneered in testing students trying out for varsity boxing, and already about half a dozen candidates have been barred from competition. It goes without saying that EEG tests would also be helpful in examining candidates for football and other major sports. In fact, brain-wave records may become part of routine medical examination for all persons and especially children (an EEG test is certainly called for after a child bumps his head severely). If Dr. Walter in England is on the right track, people who are to work together may be screened to insure that their personalities will not clash. Young couples may not have to show EEG compatibilities before they can get married, but brain-wave charts will be used more extensively for guidance and advice.

Meanwhile efforts are being made to obtain more complete records. In the average test electrodes are located at sixteen places on the scalp, and each of them picks up signals from millions of nerve cells. This is extremely poor coverage. You might as well try to sample nationwide opinions on the basis of sixteen interviews, or measure the currents of the Pacific Ocean using sixteen floating indicators. It has been estimated that really good coverage of the cortex alone would require at least a million electrodes, and the wonder is that we have learned so much using only sixteen.

Of course, a million electrodes would be impractical. But some day people having their brain waves taken may sit under devices that resemble permanent-wave machines in beauty parlors. Already Dr. John Lilly, working at the University of Pennsylvania, has used up to four hundred special micro-electrodes in animal tests. Dr. Antoine Remond of the National Center of Scientific Research in Paris is developing a radically different instrument that will furnish twenty records of the entire cortex per second. You have probably read fantasies about elaborate devices that probe the innermost secrets of the mind electronically. Science-fiction writers are still ahead of scientists, but the EEG machine of the future may represent man's closest approach to an automatic mind-reader. It will provide new facts about disease, thinking processes, personality. We have only begun to decipher the coded electrical messages of the brain.

9

SICK BRAINS

THE normal brain has been the hero of our book up to this point. Its development has been traced from a loose nerve net through ages of evolution and, in embryonic life, from egg to infant. Various chapters have reviewed some of the facts about maturing and aging in the nervous system, the mechanisms of emotion and attention, the nature of memory and prediction. From now on our chief concern will be with what happens when things go wrong, when nerve cells are injured or otherwise upset. They may be cut, crushed, infected, starved, poisoned, defective from birth or senile. Or they may be only a bit rundown. In any case, a relatively small change in the body's master organ can produce widespread and serious effects.

It is possible to detect such changes by direct observation during surgery and other methods or by post-mortem examination of nerve tissue under the microscope. But often we can make the most detailed studies and still not see anything significant. Several years ago a group of psychiatrists were having luncheon in Mory's Club in New Haven, and began reminiscing about the achievements of past investigators. The conversation turned to Konstantin von Monakow, director of the Institute for Brain Research in Zurich, Switzerland, who died in 1930 after a long and brilliant career. One of the diners praised his deceased colleague and sighed: "He must have had a magnificent brain. I wish I'd had a chance to examine it."

"I did." The remark came from a psychiatrist sitting across the table. Then he went on to give a detailed and disillusioning description of what he had observed. Although the Swiss doctor had done important work until shortly before his death, his brain had severely deteriorated and had apparently been that way for years. Autopsy revealed that it was much smaller than average and showed signs of advanced hardening of the arteries. The psychiatrist had also seen the brain of von Monakow's older brother, Nicholas, who spent the last fifty years of his life in an insane asylum. His brain was large, healthy-looking and unmarked by the effects of aging.

The visible changes in a brain may have nothing to do with how it operates. Appearances may actually lead us astray. As often as not, the damage is done deep inside nerve cells. When this happens, the results may be as invisible to the microscope as cells are to the naked eye, and we must use different instruments to detect them.

This chapter considers the general problem of changes in the brain. It discusses certain gross, easily detected changes which can produce the widest range of symptoms. It also discusses diseases for which the changes have not yet been discovered, diseases which are still the subject of controversy and superstition.

THE MANLY ART

Last year Chicago police arrested a husky twenty-five-year-old youth starting a brawl in one of the town's higher class bars. When asked to give his name back at the police station, the man peered slyly about the room and said he could not do that. His enemies were listening, ready to kill him if he told. They had followed him to the bar, disguising themselves as regular customers. They were hiding somewhere near-by. With tears in his eyes he pleaded with a police sergeant to make them stop cursing him, and calling him a has-been and a coward. He recovered after a short stay in a mental institution, but has since relapsed.

The man was a prize fighter. He was suffering from dementia pugilistica, a relatively new term in medical jargon, which has nothing to do with the general craze for fighting or the frenzied enthusiasm of boxing fans. The term refers to a malady of boxers themselves, a condition that was recognized long before the days of the Marquis of Queensberry. It means "boxing madness." The doctor who introduced it explained that prize fighters resent being called punch-drunk and suggested that they might feel better if their condition were described in Latin. Whether or not this turns out to be the case, the new term is one sign of new interest in the old problem of brain injuries in the ring.

From the standpoint of the brain specialist, this problem has certain unique aspects. Head injuries occur in a good many sports but usually, as in football and hockey, they are the result of accidents or unnecessary roughness which is duly penalized (that is, if the referee happens to be watching). But boxing represents the only popular sport in which the head is a legitimate target for attack. Moreover, self-defense has become a matter of minor importance. The average professional fighter is poorly trained. He spends little time learning the finer points of his craft. Anyway, he rarely gets ahead because of his skill in evading punches. He must be a slugger. Nowadays his success depends largely on how quickly he can knock out opponents, particularly when television audiences will switch to another channel if a fight is dull.

Punishment in the ring can produce a variety of mental upsets. It can lead to symptoms which closely resemble those of patients suffering from psychoses, major forms of mental disease. An important difference is that their attacks may not last as long, although boxers have been permanently committed to state hospitals for the insane. One boxer who lost more often than he won (the usual case) began having "blue spells" every three or four weeks. He imagined that his manager and trainers had a secret agreement with Madison Square Garden and were plotting to keep him from meeting the champion.

A New England boxer tried to commit suicide two hours after an important and bloody bout which, incidentally, he won by a knockout. He was smart enough to retire, and local newspapers came up with a collection of inside stories to explain his sudden decision. None of the stories brought up the possibility of brain damage, but several suggested that he might have lost his nerve. As pointed out in Chapter 7, memory may also be affected. When Gene Tunney was training for his second heavyweight-championship fight with Jack Dempsey, he and a sparring partner bumped heads sharply. Tunney boxed several more rounds in a complete daze. He did not remember his name when he awoke next morning, and three days later he was still unable to recall the names of close friends.

Although the attack passed before the big fight, it was one important reason for Tunney's decision to quit the ring. But the great majority of fighters do not retire voluntarily. Those who become punch-drunk often suffer from similar attacks which return at irregular intervals and may not pass so quickly. They have suffered from fits of despair and elation, hallucinations, irrational terrors, feelings of impending doom. They shift moods dramatically and swiftly. Dull and depressed one minute, they may turn violent an instant later, in or outside of the ring.

Dementia pugilistica also accounts for a great many other disturbances, involving the co-ordination of the nervous system and muscles. The typical punch-drunk prize fighter walks stiffly, "on his heels," flopping a foot or leg as if it were loose at the joint. His face becomes less expressive, particularly the eyes which have a fixed glassy stare. He slurs his words and speaks haltingly. His timing is off so that whatever skill he had in defending himself is lost. In other words, punishment makes him vulnerable to more punishment. When the vicious-circle process goes far enough, he fails to pass routine medical check-ups. He can no longer walk a straight line or swing a finger to the tip of his nose with his eyes closed.

I discussed these symptoms recently with a New York physician who has examined more than 7,500 fighters during the past twenty-five years. He has also seen the brains of men killed in the ring. To indicate what continued punishment can do to vital nerve centers, he tapped rapidly on a piece of paper with the point of a pencil until he produced a mass of closely bunched dots. "Each dot represents a tiny hemorrhage in the brain, the result of a single punch or a series of punches. As a fighter's career progresses, he gets hit more and more. If he continues fighting, time catches up with him. New hemorrhages appear near old ones until large clots are formed. At a certain stage, a fighter becomes punch-drunk. The manly art of self-defense is simply the art of producing pin-point hemorrhages in the brain."

Practically every symptom known to psychiatrists can be, and has been, produced by the effects of repeated blows on the head. An adequate blood supply is of special importance to the central organ of the nervous system. Blood brings oxygen and the brain needs plenty of it, using up one quarter of the oxygen consumed by the entire body. The two main arteries leading to your brain pass up your neck, one on either side of your Adam's apple. By pressing gently with your fingers, you can feel them pulsing with the heart's rhythm—but do not press too hard or too long.

Anything which reduces blood flow in the pipelines can bring on dizziness and loss of consciousness. They are one of the major targets in jujitsu and other techniques we have evolved to incapacitate one another scientifically. They were involved in a case which for a time baffled specialists at Bellevue Hospital in New York. Some years ago a twenty-six-year-old man walked into a clinic seeking relief from fainting spells. This is a frequent enough complaint. The puzzling thing, though, was that the attacks almost always came at formal dances and parties. The patient was shy, unmarried and "apt to be perfectionistic"—but it wasn't a neurosis.

A physical examination, and a bit of medical detective work, revealed the cause of the trouble. The patient had a tiny lump on the left side of his neck, the mark of an old and minor tuberculosis infection. Every time he put on his tuxedo to attend a dress affair, the stiff collar of his shirt pressed against the lump. The lump, in turn, pressed against the left artery and caused an irritation. The artery promptly contracted, producing a blood shortage in the brain and fainting spells. After the lump was removed, the young man continued to attend formal parties—without further mishaps.

Inside your skull the brain's arteries form a network of branches and sub-branches, a marvelous transport system that delivers ample blood to the nerve cells. The smallest branches are capillaries, microscopic tubes so narrow that your red blood cells must pass through them single file. Things are so arranged that every one of the billions of nerve cells in your head is located within a thousandth of an inch of a capillary. Considering their dimensions, these tiny blood vessels are reasonably rugged. But they can take just so much punishment and no more, and the limit may be exceeded in prize fighting.

In the beginning the concussions of frequent punches break only a few capillaries. The damage is taken care of in an efficient manner. Nerve cells in the immediate vicinity usually receive nourishment from other vessels during the emergency. They can get along on reduced rations of food and oxygen until their own pipelines have been sealed and clots are dissolved. A passing headache or dizzy spell may be the only sign of the trouble. More often than not, there are no symptoms at all. The brain heals most of its minor injuries without making a fuss about it.

But this automatic repair system is designed to handle occasional accidents. They cannot meet one emergency after the other, with shorter and shorter intervals in between (the poorest fighters receive small purses and have to fight frequently to earn a bare living). When a blood vessel that has been repaired in many places fails for the last time, other vessels take over its functions permanently. As injuries continue, the odds are that the added burden will be too much for these reserve blood channels—and things go from bad to worse. More and more nerve cells are crippled or die, because they are being deprived of normal blood supplies.

Such accelerating processes are not only a possible outcome of punishment in the ring. Time, operating without benefit of knockout punches, may produce similar results. Cerebral hemorrhage or "stroke," the condition which ended the lives of Roosevelt and Stalin, is the failure of blood vessels in the brain. Symptoms depend on where the failure is located. If it occurs in the right side of the "motor" cortex, the left side of the body may be paralyzed. Speech is affected if the damage lies in a certain area located on the left side of the brain. The patient frequently recovers from the attack and, as time passes, his symptoms disappear or are greatly reduced.

We all suffer to some degree from the repeated impacts of living. Most of us come through the ordeal remarkably well, just as most prize fighters take their batterings and do not become punch-drunk. The nervous system has many safety devices. As we have already pointed out, although its cells are not replaced when they die, other pathways may be available. Other blood vessels can take over to relieve local blood shortages which threaten to starve and suffocate near-by cells. In these ways the brain keeps its lines clear for the flow of messages that represent our thoughts and actions.

DAMAGED STRUCTURES

Like all communication networks, the nervous system is vulnerable to disorders that can be traced to uncontrolled, meaningless signals. The signals produce chaotic behavior, actions that impede rather than serve our purposes. Imagine that all the carefully synchronized stop-go lights in New York's Times Square area suddenly go berserk. Some are stuck and stay red, jamming up cars for many blocks. Others flash intermittently from red to green and back again; still others fail to light at all. The entire area is soon the scene of shouts, angry horns and a colossal traffic snarl.

Certain brain diseases involve analogous difficulties. Barrages of disturbed nerve impulses from brain to muscles account for one of the major symptoms of cerebral palsy, spasmodic and uncontrolled movements of the limbs and face. This serious childhood condition affects about twenty thousand newborn infants each year, and more than half a million Americans have been living with it since birth. It is commonly the result of brain damage suffered before or at birth, or during the early years of life. A disease of timing and adjustment in the nervous system, it indicates the importance of co-ordinating functions carried out in higher centers.

Other chapters have discussed some of the nerve structures concerned with movement. When you want a cigarette, impulses from the motor area of the cortex stream to your arms and hands— and you reach into your pocket, put the cigarette into your mouth and light up. The cortex also has its so-called "suppressor" areas whose signals prevent movements not needed during particular activities and help keep your muscles still when you are resting. The jerking movements of cerebral palsy may represent upsets in the balanced interworkings of these areas, upsets caused by damage to strategically located nerve cells. Further insight is coming from studies of the reticular formation or nerve net in the brainstem. This system plays a role in focusing our attention and pacing our physical activity.

It is difficult to describe the problems of children suffering from this disease. Try tapping the fingers of your right hand very rapidly against the top of a table and, at the same time, use your left hand to tap out a slow rhythm. You can do it, but at first you will have to concentrate fully on what you are doing. You find yourself tapping at the same rate with both hands if you relax the intensity of your attention for even a second or so. An afflicted child has the same sort of problem with the simplest movements of everyday life. Control of its arms and legs calls for enormous concentration, and a summoning of effort such as you may experience when you are dead tired and must get out of bed.

Fortunately, more and more is being done to help cerebral palsy victims—although even now only about one child out of every four receives the attention it needs. If training starts early enough, and lasts long enough, most patients will be able to find a place in society and earn their own livings when they grow up. One of the most interesting groups, a model for work of its kind, is located at P.S. 135 in New York City. Known as the Pre-School Center for Cerebral Palsied Children, it consists of a unique class of about thirty patients up to twelve years old.

In one classroom you see colored blocks, picture books, crayons and other things you would expect to see in a regular nursery school. Here the children are taught to help themselves and overcome handicaps. A teacher is busy showing a girl with a bib around her neck how to use a fork. She looks up as a boy walks slowly to the door, tries to open it and fails in the first attempt. The next attempt succeeds. She smiles: "Good for you"—and continues helping the little girl at her side. This sort of work is combined with speech training, special exercises and thorough medical and psy--

chiatric care. Carefully planned programs are designed to take advantage of the brain's powers of adjustment. When some nerve cells of the cortex are damaged or missing entirely, near-by cells may take over their duties.

Current research indicates that in the future surgery may be used increasingly in selected patients. If the nervous defects are confined to a single one of the brain's hemispheres, for example, it may help to remove the entire hemisphere. This operation was first tried about eight years ago in Johannesburg, South Africa. One of the most successful cases was that of a seven-year-old boy whose spastic movements involved the left side of his body only. The symptoms were considerably relieved a month after the right half of his brain had been removed. He was soon running about and has since responded to training far more rapidly than doctors expected.

Why should such radical surgery help? It has long been known that a man may lose half his brain and still not appear any the worse for it. You could speak with him for hours and not notice that the operation had made any difference. The most careful tests are required to reveal that his mental powers are not what they were. Part of the explanation is the fact that the hemispheres may carry out certain duties in parallel, so that if one of them is removed the work gets done just the same. But the procedure does not actually improve a patient's condition, except in the case of certain cerebral palsied children.

Our memories seem to be stored according to this general principle. The past is recorded in duplicate files, one on each side of your head. Even more important, if only one hemisphere is affected in cerebral palsy, it may seriously interfere with the workings of its twin structure on the other side. It may produce bursts of meaningless impulses. The impulses travel over the bridge of nerve fibers connecting the halves of the brain, and distort or "jam" the messages of the uninjured hemisphere. Such things may no longer happen after the affected hemisphere has been removed. This operation and others under development may bring about marked improvement, and make the long training process more effective.

Cerebral palsy is one example of the effects of brain damage in children. Other nerve diseases come later in life. Multiple sclerosis, a condition involving the destruction of the fatty white sheathing surrounding many nerve fibers, usually strikes persons between the ages of twenty and forty. One of its most famous victims was Lou Gehrig, the great first baseman of the New York Yankees. Scar tissue covers the "bare patches" of affected fibers, interferes with the normal passage of nerve impulses and leads to paralysis and other symptoms. The cure and prevention of multiple sclerosis depend on basic research to discover, among other things, why and by what process the nerve sheathing is destroyed.

Continuing research will also bring new treatments for many nervous diseases of old age. Only during the past few years have animal tests shown that brainstem injuries may produce tremors which closely resemble those found in some elderly persons. Properly placed injuries will produce practically all known nervous symptoms, and detailed maps have been prepared to show the sites of damage as precisely as Air Force maps indicate the positions of bombed targets. Such experiments indicate where trouble may be located in actual cases—which is one of the main objectives in the study of a wide variety of abnormal movements due to brain damage.

The Golden Age of Pseudo-psychology

Conditions leading mainly to mental disorders are more difficult to study. Will Rogers once said that if he ever had a mental disease he'd visit a veterinarian instead of a psychiatrist, because people who treat dumb animals know enough not to ask silly questions. Investigators studying injured nerve cells are not entirely unsympathetic to this point of view. As far as their own work is concerned, however, they find themselves in a somewhat different situation. They would give anything for an animal that cheerfully answered all their questions, even the silliest—that is, an animal other than man. Talking things over is an important aid in diagnosing mental disease and following its course, and an articulate beast might solve some of our problems.

We shall find no such creatures on this planet. Thriving chimpanzee colonies at the Laboratories of Primate Biology in Orange Park, Florida, have been given every chance to learn to speak their minds. We have books to prove that infant chimpanzees have been reared in respectable homes, according to the most liberal principles of child psychology. But they never talk. Their brains are simply not up to the feat, and they remain conversational washouts. Until chimpanzees can tell us about their operations, animal tests will continue to be of limited value in studying disturbances of ideas and emotions.

It is no wonder that our knowledge about mental illness is scanty. According to the President's Commission on the Health Needs of the Nation: "Psychiatry . . . is perhaps the most talked about, but the least understood, subject in the whole field of medicine. In knowledge useful in treating or preventing disease, it lags fifty to one hundred years behind the other major fields of medicine." We have yet to discover what happens in the brain when people suffer mental breakdowns. Yet we cannot go mad—just as we cannot suffer from cerebral palsy or dementia pugilistica—until nerve cells are dead or behaving abnormally.

This point of view need not clash with the notion that certain diseases are caused by deeply upsetting experiences during child-hood or later on in life. Such experiences can affect the brain and other parts of the body as definitely as an automobile accident. An entire branch of medicine is devoted to the study and treatment of psychosomatic illnesses, and the influences of emotional stress have been recognized for thousands of years. Conflicting ideas, problems that seem too hopelessly complicated to solve, may stir up troubles among nerve cells just as they do among nations.

A simple experiment illustrates the influence of thoughts and feel-ings, in this case the expectation of an injury that never comes. The experiment was first performed in Germany nearly fifty years ago, and has been repeated many times since. A volunteer is hypnotized and informed that his hand will be touched by a red-hot iron. He is prepared for the worst, and the worst happens. It makes no difference that the hypnotist really uses a pencil, his own finger or a piece of ice instead of a glowing brand. The effect is always the same.

The volunteer cries out in pain, and jerks his hand away. The expectation of injury is so great that it produces the exact changes in his body that a burn would produce. Colorless fluid seeps out of blood vessels in his hand, and flows into the "injured" area. The fluid produces actual blisters which last as long, and hurt as much, as those resulting from more conventional causes.

The power of suggestion and mental stresses of all kinds has been too well documented to be challenged. Every good doctor takes it into account whether he is treating stomach ulcers, heart disease or headaches. It is also a lucrative source of income to hundreds of health cultists and quacks. We look back condescendingly to the superstitions of medieval alchemists. Men who were partly scientists and partly charlatans worked in concealed laboratories and guarded their secrets as closely as the Atomic Energy Commission does today. They held strange beliefs about the things that went on in their test tubes and crucibles. Molten metal, for example, was regarded as something dead and putrefying and corrupt. The same metal, refined and hardened, was supposed to be endowed with spiritual purity. According to one historian of science, "The process was a symbol of what the age was seeking, what was found alike in Christianity and the mystery religions—death and resurrection."

Our superstitions concern mind not metal. There are alchemists among would-be mental healers today. Men posing as doctors are equally ignorant in treating patients, with far less excuse for their ignorance. This situation is discussed in an editorial, "The Golden Age of Pseudo-psychology," which appeared in the official journal of the American Psychiatric Association. The editorial notes with alarm that faked psychology is spreading, and calls for steps to stamp it out. It cites the case of an impostor who had an office in a fashionable Park Avenue apartment and passed himself off as a trained psychologist.

"Dr. X" was a smooth operator. He knew the lingo of psychoanalysis and used it generously in his own peculiar form of double talk. He would treat anything from major mental diseases to mild neurosis and plain worrying. He also dabbled in psychical research and announced that, among other things, he was clairvoyant. This claim had some truth in it. The learned doctor could predict some of his patients' future actions. An expert hypnotist, he used his skill to keep them coming back for lengthy sessions—until their money ran out or they became so sick that they were forced to see a qualified physician.

Hundreds of quacks like Dr. X are growing richer and richer, within the law. Since they do not make direct claims about treating mental disease, they are free to go ahead and treat. They listen, sympathize, scold and advise because they are not qualified to administer standard medical treatments. Their patients do not know why they are sick and are ready to blame it all on emotional disturbances. This attitude is unfortunate but understandable. After all, not so long ago doctors themselves were inclined to blame many more diseases on emotional disturbances than they do today.

Early in the nineteenth century a French physician wrote a book called *Medicine of the Passions* in which he stated that cancer of the breast was caused by jealousy, hatred and chagrin. In 1897 one of Germany's leading psychiatrists ascribed a certain disease to "competition, reckless and feverish pursuit of wealth and social position, overstudy, overwork, unhygienic modes of life, the massing of people in large cities, the indulgence in tea, coffee, tobacco, stimulants, and social and sexual excesses, and artificial modes of life." The psychiatrist, of course, was covered since the list includes about all the factors that could cause anything. But fourteen years later another specialist examined the brains of dead patients and announced a new addition to the list of causes—a corkscrew-shaped microbe or spirochete. The disease was syphilis.

Was the German psychiatrist wrong? Not entirely. But his attitude turned out to be somewhat unrealistic. Supposing the head of your local fire department decided not to bother any more about repairing hoses and engines, arguing as follows. Fires occur because the air contains too much oxygen, 21 per cent to be specific. If we could lower the proportion to the proper level, things would not burn so easily and we'd save millions and millions of dollars every year. Oxygen is the basic cause of fires. Cigarette butts, kerosene stoves, explosives and pyromaniacs are merely secondary causes. The bullet-proof logic of this argument would not keep the fire chief from losing his job or being brought to a psychiatrist.

It would be equally unrealistic to state that syphilis or any other brain disease could result from social and emotional stress—and let it go at that. Cities, sex and the high pace of living certainly have a good deal to do with syphilis, but still we can cure it with penicillin. Doctors treat people, not civilizations. They do more than investigate the possible causes of different illnesses and, together with their fellow citizens, press for reforms and new laws. They also concentrate on more immediate problems. Patients and their families are suffering and waiting for help. The volunteer who was "burned" under hypnosis feels real pain. You can explain what happened as much as you want to. You may even succeed in convincing him that it was all "purely mental," but the fresh insight is not likely to be appreciated for long. Sooner or later he will want medicine for his blisters.

Some patients see people who are nowhere about, hear voices when no one is talking, remember things that never happened. And the cortex, the eternal explainer and predictor, does what it can to make sense of its illusions, even when part of it "knows" that something is all wrong. It calls up memory traces and builds them into weird but often logical patterns. It accounts for the ghosts that have invaded its universe, and the patient explains why he is being tormented. He has committed an awful crime, or business associates are jealous of his rapid advancement, or his wife's family want to get rid of him. These fantasies should not seem too strange to us. We use similar notions, in a restrained and sophisticated fashion, to explain our own less painful illusions.

All the things that can produce severe disorders of feelings and ideas, including mental conflict itself, must interfere with the normal workings of nerve centers. An important problem is to discover where and how they interfere. The investigator's greatest fear is that he may no longer be able to learn, that rigidity of thought may set in—and not necessarily because of old age. There is always the tendency to blame the stresses of life for his troubles and those of patients, and to stop studying brains and nerve cells. The list of mental diseases, which used to include syphilis and cancer and diabetes, is shorter today than it was fifty years ago. It promises to become still shorter during the next fifty years.

It is an old question who shall decide when doctors disagree. Concerning diseases of the brain, aside from those due to obvious physical damage or those traced to missing substance, the doctors disagree. And it is in the realm of mental ills that you find the most rapidly growing point of psychiatry, the most exciting research projects. To convey anything at all about the projects one should see them through the eyes of their enthusiastic leaders. This is exactly what we shall be doing in some of the chapters to come.

10

HOW WE FEEL PAIN

Doctors at the Washington University Medical School in St. Louis are studying the strange case of an eight-year-old girl, Jane R. Jane was born without the ability to feel pain. At the age of sixteen months she fell, bumped her head severely and then went on playing as if nothing had happened. That was the first time her parents noticed anything out of the ordinary. The condition has persisted ever since. As far as medical tests and observations indicate, the girl literally doesn't know the meaning of pain.

Jane has never complained of headaches or sore muscles. Bee stings, cuts, bruises and other minor injuries do not hurt. Recently she burned her hand as she was putting a piece of paper into the fireplace. Fortunately, the burn was not serious. Large blisters appeared, however—and still she didn't cry out or suffer in any detectable way. Later she told her mother that her hand had felt a bit warm. Also, upon close questioning, she recalled "a slight pricking sensation, as if someone were just touching my skin with a pinpoint." That was all.

Similar cases are reported from time to time in medical journals. An Air Force corporal examined at the Massachusetts General Hospital passed painlessly through a variety of accidents including a deep ax wound. British case histories describe a die-caster who felt no pain—when blobs of molten lead at about 800 degrees Fahrenheit splashed against his arm—and made fun of another worker who was splashed and required first-aid treatment. Other anesthetic individuals may turn up in circus sideshows or vaudeville. Edward Gibson, a famous performer of the 1920's billed himself as "The Human Pincushion." He permitted members of the audience to stick pins into him and offered five thousand dollars to any doctor who could prove that he was suffering. (The money was never claimed.)

Offhand, you might envy such persons. The idea of going through life without a twinge or pang may seem appealing, but the record shows that the condition has many drawbacks. Life without pain is a risky business. It is something like trying to run a luxury liner without fire alarms or a bank without burglar alarms. You could get away with it, but you would be flirting with catastrophe and not even Lloyd's of London would insure you. Pain is basically a warning, a natural system of stop-look-listen signals. It helps keep us out of trouble and, when trouble comes, sends us hurrying to our medicine chests and family doctors.

Most people who never feel pain wish they did. The corporal, for example, once considered himself lucky because he never suffers from toothaches. But he has had several teeth pulled which could have been saved if he had been able to sense the familiar warning signals. It was much too late by the time he visited a dentist for a routine checkup. Regular and especially thorough medical examinations are insurance of a sort. They help furnish safeguards against the development of unsuspected diseases. But the patient can never really be sure of his health. At any time a sudden attack of appendicitis might prove fatal.

We do not yet know enough to account for human painlessness. One investigator sums up the general opinion that "the sensory defect is central rather than in the end organs or spinal cord." In plain English, nerve structures in the skin and spine are intact and the trouble is located in the brain itself. The higher structures responsible for pain may never develop completely—or their growth may be temporarily delayed and catch up later on. There are cases of children who are born without pain and gradually become more and more sensitive, until they are essentially normal. Whatever takes place in such cases, only further studies can provide a full explanation. The rest of this chapter presents some of the things we know and some current theories.

DISTRESS SIGNALS

The popular notion that a nerve is "something that hurts" has only a limited basis in fact. Most nerves do not hurt when they go into activity or are injured. Different fibers carry different types of messages—that is, they are devoted to different sensations. Irritating a particular fiber produces a particular sensation. Thus, if the optic nerve running from your eye to your brain were irritated, you might see flashes of light. Disorders affecting the auditory nerve often cause ringing or whistling sensations in the ear. Irritations of other nerves produce sensations of taste, touch, smell and so on.

Pain is a special sense in its own right, with its own mechanisms and disorders. Research is complicated by the fact that the way we react depends, to a far greater extent than most of us realize, upon emotional factors. But when you hurt yourself, the basic disturbance consists of impulses in definite pain fibers and nerve centers. Embedded in your skin, for example, are some three million "pain spots," regions which are a good deal more sensitive to pain than the surfaces immediately surrounding them. Although the skin's sense organs for pain have not been positively identified, some investigators believe they consist of microscopic clumps of tangled fibers.

The most minor mishap may start a complicated series of events in the nervous system. When you stub your toe, the first thing you feel is a sharp keen pain which comes almost immediately. The sensation results from nerve impulses flashed along relatively large nerve-fibers having diameters up to about $\frac{1}{4,000}$ inch. The fibers are express highways which carry signals moving at more than 220 miles an hour, roughly the speed of a passenger plane. These are "get away!" signals and you jerk your foot back without thinking about it. In fact, you react so swiftly that the pain sensation itself does not come until after you have taken the proper emergency measures.

Fast pain signals travel from toe to spinal cord, triggering a special reflex. Spinal nerve cells send signals to the muscles of your leg and foot, and you pull your toe away. All this takes place in less than a hundredth of a second. In other words, it takes less time than is required for the pain signals to complete their journey to the highest levels of the nervous system, where you feel pain. By the time you actually experience your hurt, by the time you yell "ouch!" your foot is already out of danger. In such cases, you react first and feel afterwards.

Another sensation comes a bit later. After the first fast pain you feel a diffuse, burning kind of pain which may linger for periods up to half an hour or so. It is produced by nerve impulses traveling in smaller, slow-traffic fibers at speeds of two to three miles an hour, about as fast as a person walks. When a six-foot man stubs his toe such pain comes roughly two seconds after the first pain. This sensation has been interpreted as a "take it easy" signal, which tells you to favor your hurt toe for a while. Incidentally, itching and tickling are believed to be special forms of "slow" pain, perhaps represented by signals traveling at even more sluggish rates.

Nerve impulses from the skin are not sensed as pain until they reach the brain—but where in the brain? Some investigators, basing their ideas on recent experiments, consider it likely that three of the higher structures may be involved in elaborating and coloring the experience of hurting. A general feeling of pain may arise after signals complete their climbs of the spinal cord and reach the upper end of the brainstem. W. K. Livingston, who runs a pain clinic at the University of Oregon Medical School, suggests the feeling may be generated in the arousal center—the reticular formation or nerve net which is concerned with keeping us awake and focusing our attention. Aspirin, morphine and certain other pain-killers act at the nerve-net level or at higher levels.

But this is not the last stop. If it were, pain would be considerably less useful as a warning signal. You would feel a vague sensation, a sort of free-floating ache which was not attached to any par-

ticular part of the body. You would not know where you were hurting. Signals must rise one level higher before you realize that the
pain is in, say, the tip of your left little finger. Pain is localized in
the thalamus, the pair of oval bodies which lies about an inch above
the top of the brainstem. Also, this center probably adds intensity
and other qualities to pain.

The sensation does not acquire its full meaning until impulses
climb another inch or two to the highest level of the nervous system.
You need your cortex to compare intensities, to tell how much more
a corn on your toe hurts than a blister on your hand. Moreover, it
is in this gray sheet of nerve cells that pain becomes the thing we
dread or accept or, perversely, seek. Pain builds up its emotional
overtones in the same ancient parts of the cortex which evolved in
lower animals hundreds of millions of years ago—and are still in-
timately concerned with our deepest feelings.

A strange story indicates the significant role which the cortex
plays in the perception of pain. A few years ago a Boston housewife
was stricken with *tic douloureux,* a severe spasmodic neuralgia of
the face and long recognized as one of the most agonizing conditions that can afflict patients. She suffered from sudden bursts of
pain in her face, intense pangs that came without warning. Drugs
were not effective in bringing the disease under control. But something had to be done fairly soon, because she was desperately
miserable and on the verge of suicide.

Surgery was recommended as a last resort. The operation was
one we will be discussing in a later chapter as a treatment for
mental disease—frontal lobotomy. It calls for the severing of certain
nerve fibers leading from the thalamus to the front part of the
cortex. This procedure, which effectively isolates that part from
the rest of the brain and nervous system, produced excellent results
in the woman's case. A week later she told her doctor that she had
been feeling fine. An enormous fear had obviously been lifted from
her mind, and she no longer complained of symptoms of any kind.

But a remarkable thing happened some time later on, during
another interview with her doctor. At one point he asked her
routinely whether the pain in her face had disappeared.

"No, doctor. It's still here," pointing to her cheek.

"Does it hurt just as much as it did before?"

"I guess so."

"Does the pain come as often as it used to?"

"Yes, doctor, it does."

The woman answered these questions in a flat, completely uninterested voice. You would use the same tone of voice if your doctor were asking you what you had for breakfast yesterday morning. Her suffering had stopped. Her pain remained, but she no longer cared.

Such cases, and they are not uncommon, show that the cortex is vitally concerned with the appreciation of our hurts. But many structures of the nervous system participate in producing the subtle experience we call pain. It may be so important as a clue to the nature of illness that in treating patients who suffer from obscure conditions doctors may have to use pain-killers sparingly—at least until the correct diagnosis has been made. For this and other reasons, it will continue to be a major subject for medical investigation.

MILLICALORIES AND DOLS

Pain research has included many efforts to measure our sensations as precisely as possible. Some of the most recent tests have been conducted by Dr. Harold G. Wolff and his associates at the Cornell Medical Center in New York. They use a special pain meter which works on the same principle a boy scout uses to start a fire by concentrating sunlight with a magnifying glass. It contains a 1,000-watt electric lamp whose rays pass through a lens and are focused sharply on a spot at the center of the forehead. The lamp can be made brighter—and the spot hotter—by turning a dial. Readings on a scale show that the amount of heat falling on the skin can be increased from 100 to 450 millicalories (thousandths of a calory).

The person being tested sits down as the dial is turned slowly. The temperature of the spot on his forehead rises little by little. He speaks up the instant he feels the first trace of pain, and the heat level is recorded. During the past decade or so thousands of such experiments have been conducted as part of a continuing project. The results do not confirm the once-widespread notion that people differ considerably in their sensitivity to pain. The great majority of persons tested at the Cornell laboratory have similar pain thresholds—that is, they vary little in the minimum amount of pain they can detect.

Most of them spoke up when the heat level was somewhere between 210 and 230 millicalories, and the odds are that your own record would fall within that narrow range. This statement holds whatever your race, color or creed. Also, there is no evidence that women naturally feel their hurts more acutely than men. As far as sensitivity to pain is concerned, the battle of the sexes is a dead heat. Age seems to make an appreciable difference. Children are more sensitive than grownups and we become less and less sensitive as we become older. Elderly persons may be difficult to treat, because they sometimes do not notice the effects of gallstones and other conditions which are extremely painful earlier in life.

Your feelings may also be more or less acute depending on where you are hurt. As you would expect, the thicker the skin the higher the pain threshold. Taking 220 millicalories as the average level for the forehead, it requires a good deal more heat—300 millicalories or more—to produce pain on calloused parts of the hands, feet and toes. The most sensitive part of the body is the cornea of the eye, the transparent layer which covers the pupil and admits light. You can feel distinct pain when this tissue is exposed to only 25 millicalories. It takes more than four times as much heat to produce a noticeable feeling in the skin just over your ribs. The palm of your hand, your foot under the arch and your forearm follow, roughly in that order.

The Cornell instrument has been used to measure the intensity of pain. After a person responds to the first threshold twinge, the dial is turned again—slowly, until he just detects the next increase of pain. Dr. Wolff reports that there are some twenty degrees of increasing pain. He has called every two steps a "dol," a word taken from *"dolor,"* meaning anguish or grief. Lists have been prepared indicating the relative intensities of a variety of common pains from mild headaches, bumped funnybones and shaving nicks (one to two dols) to burns from cigarettes and hot grease, childbirth pains and angina heart attacks (ten dols).

Although such ratings cannot be taken too seriously, the dol scale is helpful in estimating the comparative effectiveness of pain-killing drugs. Also, it indicates that there is a definite limit or peak to your ability to feel pains of rising intensity. The worst pains of all rate ten dols. After that, you feel no further increases. Another thing to notice—as far as intensity is concerned, a grease burn does not hurt any more than labor pains. The difference, and it is a big difference of course, is that labor pains last longer and cover a greater area.

Pain-meter tests confirm an old observation. If you are suffering from two hurts at the same time, the sensations do not reinforce one another. The more intense ache cancels out the less intense. As long as the pain lasts a four-dol stubbed toe will completely mask a two-dol headache, although we are not recommending the treatment. Apparently the brainstem structures which focus our attention can "concentrate" on only one pain at a time. The more intense a pain, the greater the number of alarm signals flashed to the brain from the site of the injury. In other words, the most urgent trouble stirs up the nervous system most and receives attention first. A suffering person takes advantage of this fact when he instinctively tries to blot out the pain by clenching his fists or biting his lip.

Under properly controlled test conditions, it seems that most of us are much alike in our sensitivity to pain. But the way we react, the way we exhibit our hurts to the world, is another problem entirely. Emotionally, most of us are competent and reasonably restrained actors—neither exceptionally good nor exceptionally bad. We tend to play our feelings straight. But some people, without actually realizing what they do, go in for a touch of melodrama.

I still remember my surprise at the behavior of one player on our college basketball team when he sprained his ankle. This is an occupational hazard of the game. All of us had gone through the same painful experience several times, with an occasional groan and nothing more than the usual amount of visible suffering. He was writhing and moaning in an exaggerated style so that we, his teammates, could not help exchanging small smiles even as we gathered around him. At the other extreme is the player who clamps his teeth together and hardly responds at all to an injury that would greatly affect the rest of us.

The tremendous variety of reactions is perhaps the main factor in limiting the value of laboratory studies of pain. Inevitably, there is something elusive about all our tests. The way we express our hurts is largely a matter of temperament and what we happen to be doing at the time. How you react today may depend on how you saw your parents reacting when you were a child. If you are confused or angry, if you are watching a football game or running to catch a train, you may not notice an otherwise conspicuous pain. In one pain-meter test a man completely ignored the heat on his forehead as he listened to a popular cops-and-robbers broadcast.

In fact, you commonly ignore minor pains and discomforts in the course of your daily activities. Pain is always with you or ready to be sensed, like the feel of your clothes against your body. Next time you settle back in your easy chair try the following experiment. Cross your legs and, instead of picking up the newspaper, concentrate on your position for a minute or two. In a fairly short time you will become acutely uncomfortable. You begin feeling a dull ache in your calf and foot, and soon change your position. But you would not have had such sensations if you had been reading or talking intently. Distraction may be a powerful anesthetic.

The way you earn your living also has something to do with your reactions. Severe pain may come as a shock to office workers and others who rarely suffer severe injuries because of their occupations. Farmers, construction workers and athletes tend to take their hurts in stride. One of the most stoical persons ever tested is Ted Williams, the Boston Red Sox's star hitter. Pain-threshold tests show that Williams is just as sensitive as the average person. But he did not bat an eyelash until the heat level reached more than 400 millicalories.

Other factors are even more difficult to evaluate. Pain is constantly brought to our attention in many ways. It is featured in all advertisements of aspirin and other anti-headache preparations. It is a "star" in radio and television broadcasts which present vivid portrayals of the sufferings of criminals and their victims. Such things certainly help to make us more pain-conscious and contribute to our reactions. We cannot measure their impact. Still, for all these complications and refinements, pain is usually the warning signal that nature meant it to be—at least in healthy persons.

Burning Pain

Pain, so often a sign that something has gone wrong in the body, may go wrong itself. Among the most mysterious diseases known to medicine are some of those affecting pain structures in the nervous system. The following case, reported by Massachusetts General Hospital doctors, is an example of one condition that has not yet been satisfactorily explained.

During patrol duty in Korea a twenty-four-year-old Army sergeant was hit by a sniper's bullet in the upper part of his left arm. The wound was small and clean, and healed quickly. But one symptom did not pass. A few hours after the bullet struck, he felt a burning pain in the second and third fingers of his left hand—and the suffering became worse and worse. Intense flashes of pain would flare up in his entire hand and lower forearm. It was as if a red-hot iron were being pressed down, hard, on his skin. Every nerve seemed abnormally sensitive. The slightest sensation brought on out-breaks of the searing pain—a draft of cool air, the sudden switching on of a light, a mild vibration of his bed. Once a loud noise in the next room started a severe attack.

As frequently happens in such cases, the ailment took a nasty and vicious turn. The soldier began to dread his attacks more and more so that he was in imminent danger of suffering a complete nervous collapse. And—to make things worse, if possible—the fear gradually became a "triggering" stimulus, until it was enough to produce excruciating pains by itself. In other words, intense worry resulting from the attacks could lead to fresh attacks. Finally, he became "a neurotic recluse." Terrified of anything that might aggravate his condition, he sat half-crouched and almost motionless in bed cradling his sick arm, which he kept wrapped in a moist towel.

The patient was afflicted with a condition known as causalgia, which simply means "burning pain." This disease may affect an arm or leg, and illustrates many of the things that baffle us most about pain. The injury may hurt far more or far less than we expect. More often than not a bullet does not hurt at first because the impact temporarily "stuns" nerves, blocking pain impulses. Severe wounds may heal with relatively little pain, while a minor wound leads to inconceivable suffering. Pain tends to persist long after it has any meaning or value as a warning. It may become like a "stuck" automobile horn which keeps on blowing until repairs are made. Furthermore, the longer proper treatment is delayed the more difficult it is to bring causalgia under control.

Other methods are usually required to bring permanent relief, however. Some doctors use a special basin filled with water and containing a kind of waterwheel paddle. The patient puts his ailing hand in the water and operates the paddle with his good hand. At first the slightest swirl of water may set off the burning pain. But gradually he may build up a tolerance so that more and more vigorous swirlings can be endured, which is an important first step toward a cure. Frequently it is necessary to operate directly on the affected limb, cutting selected fibers or removing certain groups of nerve cells.

Local measures, including such surgery, will work—if the disease is treated soon enough. But waiting too long brings serious complications. Causalgia is no ordinary disease, and once it gains a foothold it may become amazingly elusive. It tends to "climb" in the nervous system. Operations on the limb itself may do no good, and we have to make our incisions higher up. We may have to sever fibers in the great cable of the spinal cord. During later stages even surgery at this level may not help. The disease has moved into the highest structures of the nervous system. It is established in the brain itself, and frontal lobotomy or other operations may be necessary.

The basic cause of causalgia is still unknown. One of the most recent theories has been developed by Dr. Livingston and his associates in Oregon. According to his notions, the disease is a perversion of normal reflexes. If you are washing dishes and the water is a bit too hot, nerve signals pass up your arm along fibers leading to the spinal cord—the fibers that carry "slow," burning pain messages to the brain. Answering signals are promptly released from the cord. Traveling back to your hand along other fine fibers, they cause blood vessels to constrict. Warm blood is forced inward to deeper tissues, lowering the temperature at the surface and silencing the original "too hot" signals.

This is what normally happens. But supposing an injury—say, a bullet wound or cut in the arm—nicks the fibers that lead to the blood vessels. Now there is a hole in the covering insulation. Electricity may leak out of the fibers and flow into near-by pain fibers. The electricity produces sensations of burning, sensations which flash to the spinal cord and stimulate new "cooling off" signals destined for blood vessels in the hand. More signals leak into the pain fibers, the burning gets worse and keeps up and a vicious circle is established. A draft of air or anything else that changes skin temperature may aggravate the pain. Worrying and fear, which affect circulation in the hand and elsewhere, also send leaking signals into pain fibers.

Why does causalgia climb to higher levels? Think of the early disease as the result of a kind of whirlpool of impulses in a nerve loop that runs from hand to spine and back to hand again. Since the circling impulses sweep around through the spinal cord on every one of their laps, disturbances are repeatedly set up in the thick cable leading to the brain. As emphasized in Chapter 8 about brain waves, nerve cells are easily influenced by one another's activities. If the disturbances recur frequently enough, one vicious circle breeds another. A second whirlpool somehow becomes established in the spinal cord, and as long as the impulses continue pain is felt even though fibers have been servered in the arm. A similar spreading of electrical activity among many nerve cells could produce disturbances in the brain itself.

This theory is only one of several which are being put to the test in current experiments. When we know more about causalgia, we will be able to develop more effective measures for patients. The course of treatment, Dr. Livingston reports, "is much like the progress of a chess game. The physician makes a move and the response of his patient will determine his subsequent move. The final checkmate is likely to be the result of an intelligent campaign, rather than of a single brilliant move." The disease is a tricky and resourceful opponent, and indicates some of the subtlest and least understood aspects of pain.

Summarizing studies to date, we have found that different levels of the nervous system share in producing pain. The sensation itself may arise at one level, as a diffuse "hurting." A higher center, probably the thalamus, helps transform this vague ache into a sharp localized feeling and we know where we hurt. At the highest levels of the cortex pain becomes a complete thing. It can be compared with other sensations, interpreted, even ignored. Finally, an important way of learning more about the fundamental nature of pain is to study its perversions—and, of these, causalgia is one of the most instructive.

11

THE SACRED DISEASE

> What matter though it be only a disease, an abnormal tension
> of the brain if, when I recall and analyze the moment, it
> seems to have been one of harmony and beauty in the highest
> degree—an instant of deeper sensation, overflowing with un-
> bounded joy and rapture, ecstatic devotion, and completest
> life.

PRINCE MYSHKIN, the central character in Dostoievsky's *The
Idiot* and a victim of epilepsy, is trying to express the emotions
that come over him just before his attacks start. Dostoievsky wrote
from first-hand experience. He suffered from the disease himself
and knew that inspiration may be a prelude to convulsions as well
as to prophesies, poetry or great novels. Many epileptic patients
have similar sensations and, to a lesser degree, so do the rest of us.
Suddenly and often with no apparent reason we feel happy and
exalted, things that worried us a few moments ago seem trivial, other
people are nice-looking and pleasant and we face the day buoyantly.
We are ready to master any situation, big or small.

Imagine the same sensations intensified a thousand times and
compressed into an interval of a few seconds, and you will have some
idea of how exalted the epileptic may feel. Imagine also knowing
that almost as soon as one of these intervals arose it would be followed by an exhausting fit—and you may sense something of his

mixed raptures and fears. In earlier times such patients might have been found among soothsayers and priests, exorcising demons and hurling inkwells at devils. They believed themselves to be endowed with certain divine qualities. Their fellow men often shared the belief, and referred to epilepsy as "the sacred disease."

This name may be somewhat misleading. It recalls the fact that sufferers were occasionally honored and regarded with respect. But ignorance did not always produce respect. We have a habit of remembering the most delectable parts of medical history and forgetting its cruelties and darker aspects. As a rule, epileptics were treated neither wisely nor mercifully, particularly those who did not happen to feel exalted before their attacks. They were hated, feared, beaten, tortured, driven from village to village. Once we create gods, we must create devils as well—and we are likely to see the devils in more places and more often than the gods. Most epileptics were thought to be possessed or bewitched rather than divinely inspired.

Today we no longer consider epilepsy evil or sacred. It is recognized as a disease of the brain, a disease that can be treated successfully and sometimes cured. We study it not only to the benefit of its victims, but also to the benefit of all patients afflicted with all forms of nervous and mental disorders. Every epileptic we have tested and treated has contributed, and contributed appreciably, to our knowledge of how nerve centers work and what they do. We realize that every nervous system is vulnerable to convulsions and can tell a good deal about where the trouble is by the type of attack. The very notion of epilepsy has been broadened to include conditions which were not understood only a few years ago.

SENSITIVE CELLS

Brain waves are our most significant clues to the nature, diagnosis and treatment of epilepsy. If you ever visit a brain-wave laboratory, be sure to give the EEG machine a wide berth. Whatever you do, don't bump into it. I did once and was properly called down for it. My carelessness caused the sensitive pens to jerk sharply, as if they had been struck by an invisible hand. The result was a series of large "spikes" on the moving EEG tape—and such spikes, produced by the brain rather than by collisions, are an almost sure-fire sign of epileptic tendencies. They sometimes occur between as well as during attacks and may furnish the only objective evidence for the presence of the disease.

Epileptic spikes are massive, sudden deflections of recording pens. Like the deflections of earthquake-measuring instruments, which often are remarkably similar in appearance, they indicate that violent events are going on beneath the surface. Normal nerve cells pulse together amicably and give rise to fairly regular electrical rhythms. Behaving as predictably and dependably as any group of solid citizens, they successfully bear the brunt of everyday living and come through the experience in good shape. But the brain of an epileptic includes some cells which cannot be counted on in emergencies. They may do all right for a while, charging and discharging in unison with their neighbors. For a while they stand up to the demands of cerebral society, and we have no way of knowing them during their stable periods.

But at any time they may cause the patient's downfall. Those cells are extra-sensitive and may crack up under stress, or even under ordinary circumstances that would not affect healthy cells. Everything is calm until the last few seconds. Then the epileptic may begin to have his premonitions, his sensations of imminence. He feels uneasy or afraid and knows an attack is coming. By that time it is too late. Things have gone so far that they can no longer be brought under control. It is a period of uneasy waiting, a long tense instant before breakdown. The last inch of the fuse is burning.

Finally the explosion occurs. The sensitive cells go hog wild, releasing their electrical charges in great bursts which we can detect as spikes on our EEG records. The trouble usually starts in a small region with definite boundaries, a region which doctors call the epileptic "focus." This core of cells on the loose is a center of mayhem. It is the place we must watch most carefully to obtain a basic understanding of what epilepsy is and how it may be cured. Such cells are among the brain's most dangerous troublemakers and, like the troublemakers of real life, they may be suffering from hereditary defects, or the aftermath of infection or injury.

If things began and ended entirely within the limits of the epileptic focus, the disease would cause far less trouble than it does. But the disturbance circulates faster than small-town gossip. The rantings of a few eccentric cells may influence multitudes of healthy cells, producing a kind of mass hysteria in the brain. High-speed electrical impulses, starting from the central region, flash along nerve pathways until they reach the points where the fibers come closest to fibers of other cells. They may hesitate at these points, but they do not stop. They leap across the junctions just as sparks leap across the space between two live wires, and cause the next cells along the line to discharge. The process involves many leaps and junctions further and further away from the original source. According to one investigator, the discharges "may spread across gray matter like a prairie fire." Brain and body are whipped into a frenzy of purposeless activity, violent fits that leave the patient dazed, limp and exhausted.

People usually have this sort of fit in mind when they speak about epilepsy. But the disease often takes a variety of other forms, depending on the source and ultimate destination of the triggering impulses. Some attacks may cause so little trouble that the person never realizes he is an epileptic. His only "convulsion" may be the occasional twitching of a finger or eyelid. Although he loses consciousness many times a day, each time for perhaps a second or so, he may recover and pick up where he left off before you notice that anything is wrong. The only sign of such brief blackouts may be abnormal brain waves. The typical waves come at about three pulses per second and consist of spikes followed by hump-shaped deflections—the so-called "dart and dome" pattern.

Changes in EEG records help doctors assess the value of various treatments. Drugs are commonly prescribed for major and minor forms of epilepsy, and the ever-increasing list includes many new preparations and stand-bys like phenobarbital (which is also used in sleeping pills). Nerve cells are "fortified" by these substances and do not discharge as readily as usual. The ideal drug, among other things, would strike directly at the heart of the trouble. It would not affect healthy nerve cells and would act directly upon the supersensitive cells which make up the epileptic focus, so that they could withstand wear and tear without going berserk.

This sometimes happens, although it is more a matter of luck than wisdom. EEG abnormalities may disappear along with all symptoms. On the other hand, symptoms may be reduced or curbed entirely, and the spikes persist in showing up on the records. In such cases the ailing cells in the focus itself are probably not appreciably influenced. The drug is working on normal cells, increasing their resistance to a point where they do not respond to wild discharges. They become road blocks, and the electrical currents of epilepsy cannot spread through the brain and nervous system. We have yet to learn exactly what is wrong with sick cells, or how to put them back in working order once and for all.

Incidentally, no disease better illustrates how closely emotional stress and brain injury are related. An epileptic must be treated medically or surgically. But he may also need psychological help. The lurking fear of his next attack, the fear of being injured or shamed, can build up terrible tensions in the brain. Those tensions are electrical impulses. They roam about, bombard many cells including the sensitive ones that are least able to take it and produce attacks on their own. Given the susceptibility and the dread, a patient can worry himself into repeated convulsions. Sufferers may be appreciably improved by psychotherapy.

There is another, less comforting aspect of the situation. In an important sense epilepsy is partly a social disease. You influence and are influenced by others far more than you realize, and that includes strangers and passers-by as well as people you know. We are unintentionally responsible for a certain proportion of the epileptic's attacks. He not only dreads what is wrong with him. In fact, he is often more distressed by our reactions to his sickness. Every time we are embarrassed because we have witnessed an attack, every time we are repelled or annoyed in any way, we increase his anxiety and the odds that he will have more frequent attacks. As a specialist told me recently, "We need public understanding along with our new drugs."

PSYCHIC FITS

The manager of a large San Francisco hotel last year received a telephone call from an irate guest. The guest wanted him to send someone up to her room immediately, and find and get rid of the dead rat that was smelling up the place. She complained abusively about unsanitary conditions in the hotel and threatened to tell local health authorities all about it. The manager and the assistant manager rushed upstairs. They found only a highly excited woman who later had to be taken away by the police. There were no odors and no rats, dead or alive, in the room.

Not long ago a twenty-three-year-old nurse living in New York went into a fugue. You will find this word defined as "a polyphonic composition developed from a given theme, according to strict contrapuntal rules." When doctors rather than musicians use the word, however, they mean a sudden attack of amnesia during which the patient runs away from home. The nurse's fugue was an airplane flight to Texas. All she remembered after she arrived back in New York was that she had bought a green ticket and "a man made a pass at me."

During a recent trip to Chicago I saw a young man sitting in an EEG laboratory. The police had just brought him in and were waiting outside the door. He was an electrician and had gotten into an argument with a janitor about the payment of a bill. The man was speaking to a doctor. "Suddenly I had a gripping twisting feeling in my stomach. The feeling rose up to my head before I could do anything about it. Then everything went black. I hope you can do something for me. I need it." He had stabbed the janitor seven times with a pocket knife.

The list could be extended to fill several volumes. Veteran hotel managers have vivid memories of guests who make a fuss about unpleasant odors in their rooms. You may have noticed similar cases sniffing about in streetcars or subways with disgusted looks on their faces. Restaurant proprietors know the customer who chronically complains that the food is contaminated. Fugues are not so rare as we once believed. Good husbands have become bigamists during their amnesias. A New Haven salesman actually obtained a job with the local telephone company, and held it for more than a week before he remembered that he had another job. We have a new understanding of many bizarre and antisocial actions, and of certain types of criminal violence.

The patients we have described are all victims of "psychic fits." They may have convulsions. But often they show nothing even remotely resembling the popular notion of an epileptic attack. In times past they would have been classified as psychopaths, neurotics, schizophrenics or any one of a dozen other labels that we have invented for conditions we know very little about. Many of them are being similarly pigeonholed today. We know they are epileptics, however, because the EEG machine is not human. It simply reports what it picks up and is not misled by the prejudices built into our words. The records of these patients may include spikes and other patterns which eccentric nerve cells produce, patterns previously associated with more familiar forms of epilepsy only.

The symptoms of epilepsy, like the symptoms of all brain diseases, depend on what parts of the brain are affected. The cortex, the sheet of nerve cells that covers the brain, is wrinkled and folded. We have already seen that this surface is elaborately charted. When electrical nerve signals reach a certain tiny region on the right side of the cortex, other signals flash downward through the spinal cord to certain muscles—and the left big toe moves. Signals from a region only a fraction of an inch away move the left ankle. The next region is concerned with knee movements, the one immediately following with hip movements, and so on point by point along a narrow strip of cortex. Successive areas on the right cortex send out signals that move parts located higher and higher on the left side of the body. A complete map of the body is laid out on the right cortex and there is another map like it on the left cortex. Epileptic discharge may affect only a limited region of one of the maps, in which case a finger or eyelid twitches. They may run rampant across an entire map, producing convulsions of the opposite side of the body. Or both sides of the body may be affected when the electrical storms spread across both maps.

Sensation also has its maps on the cortex, regions where trouble may give rise to "fits" of pain, tingling and numbness at various parts of the body. The patient may hear sounds existing only in his brain, vague noises or voices that may seem to come from the right or left side of the room. He may see moving lights or a series of unrelated scenes, coming one after the other like high-speed lantern slides. One woman saw the following pictures in rapid order: Teddy Roosevelt dressed in a white vest, a pale-faced Punch bowing repeatedly, a Japanese warrior in tortoise-shell armor, Teddy Roosevelt (this time in a frock coat), a fat man blowing his nose.

Psychic fits affect the parts of the brain concerned with feeling emotion, remembering, forming associations and ideas. Such things are not mapped in fine detail. They involve large areas of the bulging front and side portions of the cortex, which evolved from ancient nerve centers designed primarily for smelling and tasting. Epileptic discharges in these areas often start with hallucinations of smell or a peculiar smacking of the lips and tongue. Then the patient loses his memory. He may wander dreamily about the house, go off on a long trip or work all day in the office (a doctor conducted medical examinations and wrote out correct prescriptions during his epileptic blackouts). He may be confused, ecstatic or enraged.

This type of epilepsy, either in its "pure" form or accompanied by convulsions, can be treated medically. New drugs help control psychic fits more effectively than anything available as recently as four or five years ago. But they may also bring on complications. If the epileptic has a mild or latent personality disturbance, it may flare up alarmingly and produce symptoms of major mental disease. One patient for example, became so depressed that instead of taking the prescribed daily doses of his medicine, he secretly hoarded the pills. Then he tried to commit suicide by swallowing the whole lot at once. Although such extreme cases are rare, there is always the chance of some lesser disorder and patients must be watched carefully.

When drugs do not help and the patient's condition is serious enough, doctors turn to more drastic measures. Eccentric cells may have to be removed from the brain surgically—and the first problem is to locate them. EEG records taken before the operation indicate their general whereabouts. Upon exposing the cortex, the surgeon may see the epileptic focus as a white scar standing out against a pink-gray background. But usually the cells that cause the trouble are not visible. In either case, electrodes are placed on the surface of the brain and in the depths to pick up brain waves directly and provide more precise bearings. Then an area including the abnormal cells is marked out and removed.

This operation was performed on the young electrician who had been arrested for stabbing a man. A week later he told his surgeon that he wanted to give up his trade and become a minister. "Here I am in bed—but what about tomorrow, next year, eternity. I think about religion all the time."

He is still an electrician. But since leaving the hospital a year ago, he has had only half a dozen mild attacks as compared with an average of one or two severe fits a month before surgery. According to latest estimates, between half and two thirds of all patients operated on are either markedly improved or, more rarely, cured completely.

FLICKERING LIGHTS

There are patients who have abnormal records and no major convulsions—and also epileptics who have convulsions and no abnormal records. As a rule, brain waves typical of the disease can be obtained simply by having the patient lie down and letting the EEG machine write its own story. But in some patients, perhaps as high a proportion as 20 per cent, the telltale rhythms fail to show up. The rhythms may be absent. Or, like the broadcast of small and distant radio stations, they may be so feeble that more powerful rhythms drown them out and our instruments cannot detect them. Special methods are called for to bring out the masked waves so that they will make their marks on the record paper.

Recently I watched doctors testing the newest of these methods at a large state hospital in the Middle West. The room was pitch dark, except for the far corner where an intense pink light was flashing on and off rapidly. The effect was like sheet lightning on a summer night. Each flicker flooded the corner with dazzling pink light, revealing a split-second glimpse of a white pillow, a green section of wall and the pale, unshaven face of the patient. After watching for a few moments, I had the sensation that the light was steady and that I was blinking my eyes.

Then the regular lights were turned on. The instrument that did all the flickering consisted of a small metal box with tube-shaped electric lamps inside and a short handle at the bottom. The lamp is held near the patient's closed eyes while the EEG machine operates (the light is bright enough to pass through the eyelids). The flicker rate is varied by adjusting a dial. In the test that had just been completed the rate had been stepped up gradually—two, three, four, five, six, seven flashes per second. The last adjustment produced the desired effect. Recording pens began jerking. Epileptic spikes began appearing on the brain-wave chart, which had previously shown normal rhythms only.

This so-called photoflash technique is simply a way of "driving" the brain, subjecting it to a bit of pressure. The flickering light enters the eye and is translated into energetic electrical pulses which stream into the cortex. A great many nerve cells charge and discharge in rhythm with the flickers. But sensitive epileptic cells cannot stand the extra strain and register their protests on the EEG tape. Similar techniques are used in more familiar medical tests. When your doctor wants to examine your heart, he may first ask you to hop up and down on one foot for a while. The idea is that if anything is wrong, the mild exercise may be enough to exaggerate significant heart sounds. Flickering light does about the same thing to the brain that hopping up and down does to the heart.

Such research has helped doctors understand cases like the following. A thirty-six-year-old woman holds a minor administrative position in one of Washington's largest Federal agencies. She works long hours, lives by herself and has few friends. Every other week end or so she catches a Friday evening train to Boston, where her father and mother live. She looks forward to these visits, and feels lonely during the return trips. Back in the Capitol on Monday morning, she often has—or used to have—"queer moods" which started at Union Station soon after she left the train. She suddenly felt worried, stopped in her tracks for a second or two and dropped things, usually her pocketbook or suitcase. Later in the morning, she occasionally had slight headaches.

Some time ago the woman was referred to a psychiatrist, on the theory that she was neurotically nostalgic for her childhood days at home. The theory hinged on the fact that her spells always occurred in Washington, never in Boston. After psychotherapy failed to produce improvement, the patient herself finally provided the missing clue to her trouble. She was discussing the spells with her family doctor and recalled that they invariably took place at a particular part of Union Station, near the end of the long outside corridor in front of the building. Then it came out that as she walked briskly past the tall stone columns along the corridor, each column blocked out the sun for an instant. Since the columns are regularly spaced, the result was a regularly flickering light. EEG studies later showed that the woman was a mild epileptic—and that she had been subjecting her brain to a solar photoflash lamp.

This unpublished case was diagnosed correctly two years ago, and many similar cases have been noted before and since. Sometimes flicker causes symptoms in persons who had never suffered an attack of any sort; sometimes it brings on spells among the nation's 750,000 known epileptics (there are many unsuspected cases). Attacks may start when a patient drives past a row of trees as the setting sun shines through. A Milwaukee insurance executive has installed "blackout" shades on the front side windows of his car, so that he is protected along a particular stretch of road on the way home. During train rides passing trees, buildings and telephone poles produce sunlight flickers and patients are often advised to pull the shades or sit on the side away from the sun.

The flickering of poorly tuned—or poorly designed—television sets may also trigger attacks. A fourteen-year-old patient was watching a cowboy program from a porch window of his house. Before anyone realized what was happening, he rushed into the living room, picked up a vase and hurled it at his sister's friend. The boy went off on a bicycle and rode around for several hours. By the time he came to, he found himself miles from home. He had suffered a psychic fit without convulsions. Another young patient, a girl, has had several attacks during broadcasts.

Investigators studying flicker-sensitive epileptics have found that red light is more likely to bring on attacks than any other color. They can't yet explain this fact, but they have taken advantage of it. Dr. Robert Schwab, head of the brain-wave laboratory at the Massachusetts General Hospital, has prescribed special eyeglasses for a girl who had been suffering from epilepsy for twelve years. These "Land of Oz" spectacles are green-tinted, so that they filter out red rays. The girl has had no attacks since she started wearing them more than a year ago. Other patients wear similar spectacles when they're at the movies or viewing television. Seeing the world through twenty-dollar, green-colored glasses is a small price to pay for fewer fits.

Unanswered Questions

How would you react to high-speed flickers? Probably the same way I did. I saw bright-colored patterns, flashing lines and circles and irregular forms which changed with each throb of the photo-flash lamp. After a minute or so, I began feeling a bit irritated, the way you might feel after working a while under flickering fluo-rescent lamps. As far as the doctors were concerned, this was a completely uninteresting reaction. More than 95 per cent of all persons tested have the same sort of sensations. But some normal persons are severely upset. One man cursed a blue streak until the lamp was switched off; others cry or become frightened. These mild psychic fits indicate that an extremely narrow line separates epileptics from the rest of us.

"Push" a nerve cell with just the right force and it flashes into action, discharging the electricity it has stored. A smaller force will produce no effects. A larger force represents so much wasted energy, because all the cell can do is release its charge—and it would do that anyway. A loaded gun is silent until you move your finger and press the trigger hard enough. Pressing the trigger harder does not increase the speed of the bullet. Guns and nerve cells either fire or do not fire.

Epileptics may have some cells which fire under relatively slight pressures. These patients are located at one end of a finely graduated scale, and we have our places on that scale. Some people live at the very edge of epilepsy; others are not quite so close to the edge; still others have an unusually strong resistance to fits of any kind. Investigators have devised an ingenious test to rate us according to our epileptic tendencies. They use the photoflash lamp together with a drug called Metrazol, which is chemically related to the camphor in moth balls. Drugs used to control epilepsy decrease the sensitivity of nerve cells. Metrazol has the opposite effect. It makes cells more sensitive and, injected in large enough doses, can produce convulsions in anyone.

Small doses increase a normal person's epileptic tendencies without actually bringing on attacks. He is now in a state where flickering light, which usually wouldn't affect him, causes his arms and legs to jerk—the harmless first signs of a full-fledged convulsion. But the convulsion does not take place, because the lamp is promptly turned off. According to reports from France, the average person must take about 50 milligrams of Metrazol, a bit more than an ounce, before he shows those first signs under flickering light. In other words, 50 can be regarded as "normal" on the epileptic scale. Levels of 0 to 10 represent "epilepsy"—that is, the light alone (no Metrazol) or at most ten milligrams of the drug will produce attacks.

The flicker-Metrazol test has revealed some new facts about who stands where on the scale. Two years ago Paris doctors began studying a group of crack airplane pilots, expecting to find that they reacted in the average fashion. These men had already passed a series of elaborate psychiatric tests. They had very fast reflexes, performed expertly in situations calling for swift decisions and maneuvers—and turned out to be surprisingly close to the epileptic in nervous sensitivity. They had a 25 rating on the epilepsy scale which means they were twice as sensitive as the average person. Many of us, especially those who learn and adapt and act rapidly, are "near-epileptics." More stolid persons, the type usually selected for submarine crews or steady routine work in business, usually find their places at the other end of the scale.

These and other experiments with the photoflash lamp show that epilepsy is not something remote and strange. It is an exaggeration of tendencies that we know are built into the brain. In a sense, we are all potential epileptics. At one time or another we have all had fleeting spells and moods which bear a suspicious resemblance to symptoms of epileptic attacks. Whenever we feel on edge, whenever we feel unaccountably irritable and excited, the odds are that groups of nerve cells in our brain are temporarily extra-sensitive. Temper tantrums, bursts of anger and laughter may be only a few steps removed from the epileptic's psychic fits.

The evidence of brain-wave records has forced us into a somewhat awkward position. We must include many dissimilar conditions under a heading that once referred to convulsive seizures and nothing else. It may be stretching things to consider epilepsy a single disease, and psychiatrists often speak of "the epilepsies." But even this change may not be enough. In the last analysis epilepsy is probably not a disease at all. It may turn out to be a symptom, the result of the antics of ailing cells. We shall have to go more deeply into the chemistry of those cells before we can properly classify our varied and complex fits.

12

THE RIDDLE OF NEUROSIS

Ancient mapmakers had a simple way of marking unexplored territory, which made up most of the earth's surface. Across appropriate parts of their maps they wrote the words "Here Are Dragons," sometimes emphasizing the point with illuminated illustrations of fire-breathing monsters. Such labels made it clear that the mapmakers knew nothing about the territory or what was going on there. The brain, like the world of the ancients, has its unexplored territories which we tend to populate with things no less fantastic than dragons. The presence of dragons may be a useful hypothesis. For one thing, it can help prevent us from entering places we are ill-prepared to enter. But if it does little more than discourage explorers, it is hardly worth its keep.

Many elaborate myths have been created about the workings of the brain in health and disease. Among the most persistent are those which concern the baffling disorders known collectively as neurosis. The big problem does not involve factors that may start the trouble, the triggering causes of neurosis. In a sense, we are already burdened with too many of them. We know that defective heredity, infection, injury and—above all—emotional stress can lead to breakdown. But we do not know what effects they produce in the nervous system, or what is happening in the patient's brain. Current theories are not supported by the results of controlled scientific tests.

What is the continuing cause of neurosis, the process that keeps on going even after the original source of the trouble has vanished? Cancer investigators are asking themselves the same sort of question. They, too, are burdened with an excess of triggering causes. Diet has something to do with cancer. The disease has been started by X-ray and radium poisoning, long-term exposure to intense sunlight and inhaling irritating fumes and dusts. But the thing that persists, the thing that doctors must treat, is a mysterious and continuing growth of cells. Neurosis is also the result of a continuing, self-feeding process. Until we understand that process better, however, we shall probably have to make the best of our myths and use modern equivalents for the ancients' "Here Are Dragons."

This chapter is concerned with an approach which many people expect will yield new and more effective treatments for neurosis. It presents the viewpoint of the brain investigator who is not primarily interested in egos and ids, father- or mother-images, Oedipus complexes and other concepts of psychoanalysis. He sees nerve cells and nerve fibers under the microscope, and measures their electrical signals with brain-wave machines. He studies the chemical and physical changes, the movements of electrically charged particles, which produce those signals. People like him, guided by similar attitudes and using similar techniques, have been leaders in advancing the frontiers of medicine.

Many of the psychiatrists I consulted are convinced that the treatment of certain neuroses will change radically within ten years or so. They speculate about drugs to stop anxiety the way novocaine stops pain. But there are no such drugs now. The study of neurosis is one of the most active fields in psychiatry, and that means many treatments are being tested. We have simply selected a few as examples of a significant trend.

A MATTER OF DEGREE

Neurosis may appear in many forms. It may develop gradually or come swiftly and suddenly like an attack of infantile paralysis. Strictly speaking, there is no such thing as immunity. Judging by the evidence accumulated during our world wars, anyone can break down providing the circumstances are rigorous enough. In the words of one leading psychiatrist, military experience indicates that "the best of us have neurotic possibilities." Of course, some people seem to be more resistant than others, but neurosis affects something—some mechanism or complex of mechanisms—common to us all. Between 1941 and 1946 Army doctors treated more than 750,000 soldiers suffering from personality disorders.

Meanwhile neurosis was also prevalent among workers in the factories of all nations. A British survey revealed that it affected one out of every ten employees and was responsible for a quarter to a third of all absence due to illness. As you might expect, neurotic disturbances were particularly frequent among men and women who worked on assembly lines and had to go through the same motions over and over again. Repeated tasks, involving the repeated transmission of nerve signals along the same pathways, apparently throw something out of adjustment in the brain. Monotony has long been recognized as a powerful factor in neurosis—that is, monotony which we can do little to counteract.

In peaceful and prosperous times one may drop a boring job or demand shorter hours and higher pay. But during the war workers tried to stick to their jobs and keep their worries to themselves. Worry is a signal of a sort, a signal that calls for action. Doing something, even the second or third best thing, is usually far more effective than brooding and doing nothing at all.

Mark Twain used to tell a story about himself which illustrates the psychological value of going into action when we are troubled. One summer night he tumbled into bed, dead-tired and determined to catch up on his sleep. But he could not fall asleep. The weather was hot and humid, and to make matters worse the only window in the room was stuck fast. After tossing about for a time, he realized that unless he opened it he would have little rest. So he got up, and began pounding and tugging at the window in a desperate effort to let in some fresh air. The window remained stuck. Back in bed, Mark Twain endured the stuffy atmosphere of the room as long as he could. Finally he picked up a shoe from the floor, hurled it toward the window and sighed with relief as he heard the sound of breaking glass. He was sleeping soundly a little while later. Next morning he awoke—and found the window still intact and still closed. The shoe had missed its target and crashed into the glass of a near-by bookcase.

For some people there is no equivalent to the throwing of a shoe. They cannot make certain decisions, or are frustrated in their attempt to solve their problems. For example, there is the recent case of a New York contractor who had been living with an alcoholic wife for more than twenty years. All the treatments known to medicine had failed to help her, and now he had become a patient himself. He lived in a constant state of fear and would start violently at the slightest noise. When he was walking on the sidewalk, the sound of an approaching truck or an airplane overhead would terrify him so that it was all he could do to keep from running away in panic. The patient was suffering from what psychiatrists call an anxiety state, a common form of neurosis which affected many soldiers in the last war. This condition is an exaggerated version of anxieties we all experience from time to time. Only in extreme cases do such feelings persist and dominate us.

Another type of neurosis includes victims of obsessions and also represents an exaggeration of normal behavior. The average housewife is quite uncomfortable when she walks into a messy room and, if it's her own room, she won't relax until she has a chance to clean it up. Many businessmen and office workers react the same way to desks piled with papers and sloppy file cabinets. We all have our pet obsessions—the mess in Washington, writing poetry, gardening, bringing up children, the importance of toothpaste or whatever else we are selling. If you were not a bit obsessed about something, you would be an extremely unproductive person.

Carry this tendency only a step further, and you are already among neurotics and near-neurotics. You have the man who can't eat without first peering at his knife and fork and then wiping them to make sure they're not dirty—or the hostess who keeps her living room pathologically neat and spotless, so that you feel like a clumsy tramp every time you sit down. She watches you flick your cigarette into the nearest ashtray, and soon she is making her rounds emptying it and all other equally contaminated ashtrays. This does not mean that all highly fastidious persons are ripe for psychoanalysis. But if cleanliness is next to godliness, overcleanliness is only one step removed from neurosis.

Patients afflicted with more severe obsessions feel compelled to repeat the same act over and over again, and can do nothing to stop themselves. A psychiatrist told me about two such cases recently. One man keeps ducking his head every morning while he shaves himself, because he is afraid that some day he might straighten up suddenly and injure himself by striking the corner of the medicine chest. The other patient, a prominent woman's club leader, is obsessed with the notion that she might swallow some boiling hot fluid and burn her stomach. She takes her tea or coffee teaspoonful by teaspoonful, blowing hard and loud before each sip just to make sure it is cool enough. Although the noisy habit causes her considerable embarrassment, she is unable to break it.

Hand-washing is one of the commonest and best publicized forms of compulsive action. Patients who do it are usually suffering from a guilty conscience like Lady Macbeth, the most famous of all fictional hand-washers. As a rule, however, they have far less to be guilty about. An income-tax expert served in the infantry for four and a half years during World War I and came through the experience unharmed, physically or mentally. His trouble started on the way home when he had his first and only sexual experience with a prostitute. The next day he began to worry about catching a venereal disease and soon he was washing his hands thoroughly every half hour or so. The habit has continued ever since, although it has been tapering off during the past few years. For some reason obsessed patients are extremely difficult to treat. But they often improve as they get older and care less deeply about more things.

For practically every familiar trait of human personality there is a neurotic counterpart; a disease in which the trait has become the core of the problem. No matter how restrained or retiring you are, you probably find yourself showing off and being melodramatic from time to time. The tendency to act a part is magnified in the hysterical patient, who weeps easily or displays other emotional fireworks, especially when other people are watching. When you are nervous or tired your speech stumbles and you hesitate in getting words out, a difficulty which takes on extreme forms in neurotic stuttering.

With nationwide organizations launching annual drives to help victims of heart disease, tuberculosis and a dozen other conditions, we are more aware than ever before of general medical problems. And we probably worry more about our own health. This type of self-concern reaches a high pitch in the hypochondriac, who rarely feels real pain but nags querulously about a wide variety of vague discomforts inside his body. Neurosis is a caricature of things that generally pass for normal behavior. It is not always easy to detect. Severe cases, probably about 2,500,000 patients, can usually be diagnosed readily. But in the spectrum of nervous behavior there is a fuzzy region between "perfectly normal" people (a sparsely populated category which has been estimated to include only a million Americans) and people like the overtidy hostess with minor eccentricities and mild symptoms. The latter group includes most of us.

GAS FOR NEUROSIS

Among the various available treatments for neurosis, psychoanalysis has received by far the most attention. Many books and magazine articles, prepared by patients and professional writers as well as specialists, describe what happens during long sessions with analysts and the theories which have been formulated in an attempt to explain the results. But neurosis is also being treated by other methods. I saw one of them being used in a doctor's office overlooking Lake Michigan in Chicago. It was the private office of Dr. L. J. Meduna of the University of Illinois Neuropsychiatric Institute. Dr. Meduna is internationally known as the psychiatrist who discovered that artificially produced convulsions can be used to treat mental disease (this treatment will be discussed in the next chapter).

The room contained a desk, several chairs, a hospital-type bed against the wall. The only unusual equipment consisted of two torpedo-shaped gas cylinders like the ones park vendors use to fill toy balloons. I had come to see the gas in those steel cylinders being used for an entirely different purpose—the treatment of neurosis. The patient, a slender pleasant-looking man, smiled at me as he entered the room. He knew I was writing a book about the brain and had given his permission for me to sit in on the treatment.

He took off his coat, loosened his shirt and lay down on the bed. A compact rubber inhalator, resembling the breathing apparatus designed for underwater swimming, was placed over his nose and mouth. Then Dr. Meduna turned on the gas, telling the patient to breathe deeply. At first the breaths came regularly as the doctor counted aloud "One, two, three. . . ." But soon the counting speeded up. The patient was unconscious now. He breathed faster and faster, panting and heaving as if he were running. He started sweating, his lips trembled, his legs twisted slowly. His hands, previously relaxed, clenched so that the knuckles showed white. He inhaled twenty times before the gas was turned off, and regained consciousness within a few seconds.

The patient told me about himself a short time afterwards. He was forty-one years old, worked as an accountant for a chain of grocery stores and had stuttered badly ever since childhood. Doctors said his speech affliction, like most such cases, was due to psychological causes. "I decided to become an accountant, because that meant I'd spend most of my time dealing with figures and wouldn't have to speak to so many people. Just a few months ago a man stopped me on the street and asked me for fifty cents to buy a drink. I was so surprised at his nerve that I went with him to a bar. Also, the doctor told me to practice talking and I like to talk with strangers. They don't know me and I feel better with them.

"This time a funny thing happened. After the panhandler heard me trying to talk, he felt sorry for me—and bought me a drink. That should give you an idea of how terrible it was. I'd stutter every other sentence or so. It came suddenly, explosively, and I'd get all tied up with cramps in my face muscles. I used to fight it. I wanted to tear at my throat it made me so mad. Of course, that made it worse. Now I'm relaxed. I don't care. I know I wasn't talking so well to you a few minutes ago, but I know I'm getting better and don't worry about it."

The accountant had just gone through his nineteenth two-minute gas session. His treatment ended six months ago after fifteen more sessions. The only trace of his old affliction is a slight speech hesitation when he's highly excited. His severe stuttering has disappeared. I watched other people being treated—two women with migraine headaches, another stutterer, three hysteria patients. There were also several sufferers from anxiety neurosis, including a woman who moaned and cried out while she was unconscious from the gas and told me she hadn't been able to breathe easily for years after her father's death. In all, I saw about a dozen patients within two hours. The treatments consisted of fifteen to thirty whiffs of gas.

Dr. Meduna uses a mixture consisting of 70 per cent oxygen and 30 per cent carbon dioxide (air contains 21 and .03 per cent of the gases respectively). Carbon dioxide is the main ingredient of the simple recipe. This is the waste gas you exhale, the gas that plants "inhale" to make chlorophyll for toothpastes and deodorants, the gas that forms the bubbles in soda water and champagne. Its effects on the nervous system are widespread and complex. Controlling it is one important problem of the designers of the U.S.S. *Nautilus,* the first atom-powered submarine. Carbon dioxide tends to accumulate during long periods of submergence, as chemical absorbers which extract it from the air become saturated, and it produces mental and emotional disorders. Such conditions were reported frequently among submarine crews during World War II.

But somehow higher concentrations of carbon dioxide, inhaled rapidly, may be effective as a measure to combat neurosis. Dr. Meduna first used the treatment during the war when he was doing research for the Army's Chemical Warfare Service. Certain studies had focused his attention on drugs that affected the hypothalamus and other deep-seated brain centers which he believed to be possible sites of neurotic processes. Then one day he remembered a report published more than a quarter of a century ago.

Investigators in Wisconsin had tried carbon dioxide on mental patients without success, but they had confined their tests to victims of schizophrenia and other major mental diseases. Dr. Meduna tried the same general procedure on neurotic patients.

To date he has treated more than five hundred patients, for an average of forty sessions each and some twenty-five inhalations per session. Carbon dioxide is no cure-all. Like psychoanalysis, it does not help most obsessive patients or severe hypochondriacs (fortunately a small proportion of neurotics), or patients who have been in hospitals for years. It does not help submissive homosexuals, patients of either sex who play the woman's role, although for some reason it may be used to treat domineering homosexuals. Eight per cent of patients who improved became worse a year or more later, and the relapse rate may turn out to be twice as high. But allowing for this fact, about two out of three of Dr. Meduna's patients have been treated successfully.

Such results cannot be accounted for purely on the basis of suggestion, the powerful healing effect of a patient's faith that he will be healed. Dr. Meduna and other psychiatrists have given mock treatments to groups of neurotics. The patients did not know they were being used as "controls." The medical routine was unchanged —the same reassuring words, the same rubber inhalator, the same hiss of gas escaping from steel cylinders. But the gas was not the same. Certain patients received mixtures containing 5 instead of 30 per cent carbon dioxide; others inhaled nitrous oxide, the dentist's laughing gas. Some patients improved during the early stages of the control tests. But every single one of them relapsed to their former state after thirty to forty sessions. The evidence is strong that carbon dioxide, by affecting nerve cells in the brain, can produce relief from neurosis.

Dr. Meduna's patients are only a small proportion of the total treated by other psychiatrists at other institutions. Recently, and particularly during the past three or four years, carbon dioxide has been tried on a larger scale than ever before. It has been tested at the New York University-Bellevue Medical Center, the Montreal Neurological Institute and other hospitals in the United States and abroad. The list also includes state and Veterans Administration hospitals, and many doctors who administer the gas in private practice. Further research is clearly called for, because some contradictory results have been reported. But more than ten thousand patients have been treated to date, and carbon dioxide may indicate one line of future progress.

Another method, also developed during World War II, involves the use of barbiturates and other sleep-producing drugs. After receiving just enough medicine to make him drowsy, the patient behaves very much as if he had been hypnotized. Under the prompting of a psychiatrist, he may act out terrifying events which might not be recalled without the aid of drugs. The use of this technique, followed by interviews, has benefited many patients and the search for more effective drugs is continuing.

One of the latest and most interesting studies is under way at the New York State Psychiatric Institute and Columbia University's College of Physicians and Surgeons. They have given neurotic patients pills containing new antihistamines, close chemical relatives of the preparations used to curb the symptoms of colds and hayfever. The drugs, which were first tested by French doctors, seem to be effective in reducing tension and anxiety—at least in preliminary trials.

Vicious Circles

We do not know how these newer treatments work, when they work. But one theory is based on observations of patients suffering from causalgia, the persistent burning pain discussed in the preceding chapter. What does burning pain have to do with neurosis? For one thing, both disorders are exaggerations or perversions of normal processes. In causalgia a normal warning pain is turned into an agonizing, unceasing affliction. In neurosis worry is similarly transformed. Worry or anxiety can be regarded as a kind of mental pain, and its perversion may be neurosis. When you are worrying, when you are thinking or acting or feeling in any way, electrical impulses are passing along nerve fibers in your brain. As long as you worry, these impulses keep flashing like a burglar alarm. When you do something about it, they stop—that is, under normal circumstances.

Imagine that a nerve channel running from cell A to cell B in your brain is your "worry" pathway. You are driving your car fast, trying to make an appointment at the office. Time is getting short and there is no clock in sight. The worry pathway is jammed with electrical impulses that represent your concern about being late. Suddenly you see a clock. You have plenty of time and forget your worries. Somehow the sight of the clock produces nerve signals that "shut off" electrical activities in cell A. Although the two-cell pathway is an oversimplification of the actual nerve networks, the general idea holds. You are upset as long as nerve signals flash through certain fibers in the brain, and no longer.

But if signals that would normally stop the process fail to do so—if they aggravate rather than inhibit the nerve cells involved in worrying—the result may be neurosis. The process feeds itself. You see a messy ashtray, are mildly disturbed and empty it. The act quiets complaining nerve cells, and that is that. The neurotically inclined hostess does exactly the same thing, but it brings her no peace. She still fidgets and watches like a hawk for the ashtray to get dirty again. The rumble of an oncoming truck may make you edge away from the street side of the pavement. A victim of anxiety neurosis feels panicky. A handsome raise that would make you feel fine, merely goads the neurotic go-getter, the man chronically on the make, into increased envy of those still outearning him.

Neurotics are driven to avoid something, to escape whatever it is that torments them. They do irrational things, because running away can make all of us irrational. A person on the attack, and literally on the attack, comes in with his fists flying and is in full possession of his faculties. Above all, he uses his vision, the most valuable human sense, to get at his opponent. A person fleeing in panic turns his back on the cause of his fear and cannot see it. He depends mainly on sound, the thuds of pursuing feet, for his salvation—and that sense is far less precise when it comes to keeping track of danger. He runs blindly. He may run in circles or into an even worse situation, from frying pan to fire. Neurotics usually run away in a figurative sense only, but their panic fails them in similar ways.

One eighteen-year-old girl broke down after the death of her mother. She tried to avoid persistent thoughts about the funeral by concentrating on gay things. At first it was flowers. She talked about flowers, dreamed about flowers, bought flowers and even had her wallpaper changed to a type with flowery designs. The obsession worked for about three months. Then everything was spoiled when she suddenly recalled that flowers are used at funerals. So she shifted the direction of her escape, changing her obsession and all its symbols including the wallpaper. She thought incessantly about diamonds until another connection forced her to change again— diamonds have facets like the edges of a coffin. Since then she has tried and discarded many obsessions. Now, at the age of fifty-two, she is obsessed with the number 14, for some reason known only to herself. She avoids flowers, diamonds and a long list of other normally pleasant things that bring back thoughts about her mother's death.

The causalgia patient also becomes a chronic avoider. The thing he tries to avoid, of course, is the burning pain and anything that he fears will bring it on. As the disorder progresses, his symptom is aggravated by more and more sensations which normally do not cause suffering. At first a light touch on his hand or a breath of cool air may cause the pain to flare up. Later noise, light, excitement, any sudden movement and many other factors may produce the same effect. The patient seeks to avoid all normal sensation in his affected hand. He keeps it wrapped in moist towels, shields it with his body and good hand.

In trying to save himself he narrows his world of experience and behaves irrationally. He may protest vigorously when the doctor wants to examine his hand, bending over it protectively and refusing treatment. This reaction resembles the well-known resistance of the neurotic who fights efforts to get at certain memories which have become inaccessible. If the victim of burning pain can be persuaded to endure his suffering for a while, if he can stand up for a while to the agony that a light touch may bring, he is often well on the way toward recovery. The neurotic who manages to over-come his resistance to treatment may also be treated successfully.

The interesting similarities between the conditions add up to one thing. The same basic process underlies both disorders—the persistent circling of signals in nerve loops, a kind of electrical whirlpool. In burning pain the process starts in a limb and affects nerve fibers concerned with pain. In neurosis the process starts in the brain and affects fibers concerned with worry, fear and other emotional disturbances. In both diseases the earlier the treatment, the better the chances of putting a stop to the signals and work-ing a cure. It may be too late once the process establishes itself in the nervous system. Burning pain may be caused by short circuits in injured nerve pathways. Things are rarely that simple in neurosis, but the result is probably similar. Malignant, persisting worries are electrical whirlpools in the brain.

This theory is the product of many minds. The basic idea of signals circulating in nerve loops was first discussed in 1929 by Dr. Lawrence S. Kubie, a New York psychoanalyst. Dr. Lorente de No of the Rockefeller Institute for Medical Research discovered that such loops actually exist in the nervous system. As pointed out in the preceding chapter, Dr. Livingston has used the notion in ex-plaining burning pain. Dr. Warren McCulloch—one of the two investigators whose struggles to tame the wild chimpanzee, Maggie the Thirteenth, have been described—has played a leading role in synthesizing these and other observations and in applying them to an analysis of neurosis.

Like all theories, the vicious-circle theory of neurosis is tentative and will be modified or discarded when it is no longer useful. But it represents an important and stimulating attempt to get at the physical basis of an extremely common type of brain disorder. For example, the theory offers some insight into the possible effects of carbon dioxide. The gas temporarily "dopes" brain cells, includ-ing those which may be overactive when we are afraid or miserable, slowing them down so that they respond less vigorously to nerve signals. In other words, it can be an anesthetic for worry (so is alcohol, but we drown our sorrows at the risk of becoming addicts).

It may work by blocking cells in overactive nerve loops and thus stopping the flow of circling signals.

The nature of neurotic symptoms depends on what part of the brain is affected. Various things may happen if the trouble exerts its main influence on the hypothalamus at the upper end of the brainstem. The middle and back portions of the nerve center go into action when you become excited or jittery. According to Dr. Meduna, disturbances in these regions are often responsible for the fear and panic of anxiety neuroses. The front part of the hypothalamus produces opposite effects, lowering blood pressure and generally relaxing the body, and may be especially involved in such conditions as neurotic impotence, frigidity and spastic colon. Obsessions, stuttering, tics or nervous muscle twitches may be signs that nerve whirlpools have become established among the complex pathways of the cortex, the brain's highest center. Whether or not these particular speculations are confirmed, they indicate some general lines of future study.

LIVING TOGETHER

The future may teach us how to exercise a direct influence, by means of particular chemical substances, upon the amounts of energy and their distribution in the apparatus of the mind. ... But for the moment we have nothing better at our disposal than the technique of psychoanalysis and for that reason, in spite of its limitations, it is not to be despised.

In these words Freud foresaw the possibility that neurosis might eventually be treated with medicines like other diseases.

But neither drugs nor psychoanalysis can be expected to remedy the human situations out of which disorders frequently arise. Wherever love fails, wherever bonds are broken between individuals of a family or community, you are apt to find neurosis. We have seen this happen among the Welsh coal miners of Great Britain. Part of their story is told in *How Green Was My Valley*. For generations they lived together in small villages, went to school together, worked together. Then things began changing. Automobiles and faster trains made the village more accessible. Easy-to-get-at coal was running out, and expensive new machinery had to be moved in to help do the mining. Strangers arrived with the machinery, and the miners had a deep-rooted hatred for what they did not know or understand. Fifty years ago neurosis was rare among the miners. Today it is a leading cause of absenteeism.

Before the war British psychiatrists predicted that air-raid casualties would include a high proportion of mental patients. Their expectations were not confirmed when the Nazi blitz came. Children and parents stood up amazingly well to the stresses of large-scale attacks—as long as they were living together. But here is the sort of thing that happened when families were broken up, as described in "War and Children," a report by Dr. Anna Freud about wartime nurseries in England.

Patrick was three years old and slept with his parents in one of London's subway stations. But after he got measles, his parents decided to send him to a healthier place in the country. They promised to visit him if he didn't cry. The child nodded and promised he wouldn't. Three days later at the nursery he began nodding automatically like an animated display-window dummy. As he nodded, he repeated the same words over and over again: "My mother will put on my overcoat and my leggings, she will zip up the zipper, she will put on my pixie hat and she will take me home again." He stopped talking when he was told to, but his lips kept moving and he made gestures of pulling the zipper and putting on his pixie hat. Patrick's neurosis vanished when his mother took him home again.

We do not yet fully appreciate how closely we are bound to other people, how much what we do depends on what they do. Neurosis furnishes some hints and will furnish more when we understand it better. There are other hints, ranging from everyday observations to the reactions of mobs and crowds. Contagious yawns and continuous coughing among waiting audiences are common signs of our sensitivity to the behavior of others. Mass hysteria is a more dramatic symptom. Not long ago a large group of high-school girls in Natchez, Mississippi, were cheering at a local football game. Two girls fainted from the excitement and the hot sun. Several girls sitting near-by saw them faint and promptly fainted, too. Within ten minutes the fainting had become general, and by the time things calmed down 165 girls had been taken to the hospital.

In the past similarly excited crowds have seen sea serpents, ghosts and other eerie beings. Nowadays news travels faster and we can produce mass hysteria at a distance. Orson Welles' broadcast about a fictitious invasion from Mars aroused panic in thousands of listeners, and currently we have our tales of flying saucers. The point at issue is not the reality of ghosts, Martians or flying saucers but the extent to which we are affected by other people. Social science, when it grows up, may have as much to tell us about normal behavior and neurosis as biology and medicine. We have yet to learn what living together really means.

13

A VISIT TO MANTENO

I<small>T WAS</small> Sunday morning at South Chicago's Greyhound bus terminal. The terminal was jammed, especially in front of the gate for the St. Louis bus. But only a few of the passengers were going all the way to St. Louis. Practically every one of them had a round-trip ticket for Manteno, a small town about fifty miles from Chicago and the site of the Manteno State Hospital for the mentally ill. They kept coming, filling the regularly scheduled bus within a few minutes. By starting time, 10:30 A.M., four extra buses were called up to take care of the crowds.

I sat next to an elderly woman near the front of the first bus. We had been riding for about ten minutes or so when she reached into her pocketbook, pulled out an old watch wrapped in a handkerchief and put the watch to her ear to make sure it was running properly. Then she asked me whether I had the correct time and began talking. It was her daughter who had been out of her mind for more than four years. She visited the hospital three times a week and her sister helped by giving her money for the trips.

Each trip cost $3.11, and there were extras. Sometimes she saved enough to bring candy to the nurses because they treated her daughter so well. Sometimes they had parties for the patients and she bought decorations and, now and then, a small gift. She didn't know why her daughter had become sick. There had never been any trouble in the family or at school. Her two sons were not sick and her sister's daughter was married and had two children. Her daughter had been a beautiful child. "Now she doesn't know who I am. But she likes to see me, and sometimes she remembers that I've been there before."

Many other passengers on the bus knew that they, too, would not be recognized. Many were uncertain as to what they'd encounter—the panic, the confusion, the wild accusations, the terrible despair of a deranged husband, wife, father, mother. Or would the patients smile, speak as rationally as if they had never been sick and plead convincingly to be allowed to come home? But visitors go home alone in the evening. They go away touched with the hope or despair of the people they love and must leave behind. Sunday is the big visiting day at two hundred odd state hospitals throughout the United States where doctors, nurses and attendants attempt to treat more than 750,000 severely ill mental patients.

Alone Together

I visited Manteno for several reasons. For one thing, it is one of the nation's largest and better-run mental institutions. Moreover, during recent years considerable progress was made there under the leadership of Dr. Alfred P. Bay, the superintendent and a professional state-hospital administrator. I lived the better part of a week at Manteno, staying in the doctors' quarters on the grounds. I attended staff conferences on special cases and watched routine and experimental treatments of various sorts. But most of my time was spent in the wards, seeing and speaking with patients, men and women, newcomers as well as veterans who had been at the hospital fifteen or twenty years.

At first impression a mental-hospital ward may not strike visitors as unusual in any way. Certainly there is nothing sensational or spectacular about the early stages of the experience. The strangeness makes itself felt gradually. People are talking, walking about, reading, playing cards or simply sitting still. You see them doing things the way they would do them at home. Then you begin to realize how peculiar that is. Imagine that a person were suddenly taken out of his home, placed in a large room together with fifty or more individuals from as many different families—and went on behaving almost exactly as he had been when he was whisked away from his living room.

Entering a mental ward is something like breaking in upon many privacies at once. People are smiling to themselves, muttering, sobbing as if they were alone. And they are alone, so much so that they never really act or feel together. The fact that they are rugged individualists with a vengeance often makes it possible for one attendant to take care of a large group. Occasionally there is a stir in the atmosphere when the doctor or a visitor comes in, or some patient suffers an unusually violent emotional upheaval. But it is a tenuous and indefinite sort of communication, like the uneasy feeling during an off day at the office when everybody is on edge and everything seems to go wrong. Mental patients do not have to be kept in solitary rooms. They are alone together.

When you speak with them, you may or may not be aware that they are mentally ill. A large proportion of patients do not trust themselves or you, and manage to avoid revealing their thoughts and feelings most of the time. For example, a Manteno psychiatrist introduced me to a woman dressed in a green sweater and dark blue slacks. She was thin and tired-looking, about thirty-five years old and ready to talk. She was interested to hear that I was writing a book and told me she did a good deal of reading, especially about history and politics. After a few minutes, I asked her why she was in the hospital. She told me she had been very nervous and her husband had sent her there.

Then she started talking about other things. Later I asked the same question several times, again without learning anything new. At last, she told me what had made her nervous. "My five-year-old daughter used to sing all the time while she played. When it all started, she stopped singing every time I came into the room. She became tense and nervous when I was around. This may seem unbelievable to you, but she spoke in a strange language and arranged her toys in patterns. The patterns were codes. She was sending messages."

What were the messages about? "Military strategy, of course. They were messages to Eisenhower about Korea. You wouldn't believe it if I told you what they were about, but they were very important. Top secret. I understood them. But my daughter is just a little child. She's smart and talented, but how could she know all about military affairs and what was going on in Korea? I don't understand that." The patient had finally given herself away, but not until we had talked for more than three quarters of an hour. And, at that, I had the advantage of knowing she was diagnosed as a schizophrenic, and of seeing her record beforehand. (She lived opposite a factory and, among other things, had smashed the windows of cars belonging to the workers, whom she believed were Nazi agents.)

Of course, many inmates are obviously sick, particularly the ones kept in violent wards. More often than not, however, they seem quite normal. The odds are that you could converse with them for long periods and never realize they were sick. The appearance of sanity represents the mental patient's effort to fit into a world that rarely makes sense to him. But it only masks his terrible aloneness.

The psychotic, the victim of major mental disease, is sicker than the neurotic. The neurotic can usually make some sort of social adjustment. He can get along with most other people, hold a job, obey laws. He is sick, but sick in a real world. He may have an abnormal fear of being shut in, of sitting with his back to a corner. But he knows it is a real corner in a real room, and can describe his feelings in meaningful terms. The psychotic lives in a distorted world. His "corners" may not exist, but he is cornered just as surely and can do little about it. His hold on reality has slipped. A sofa is a "coffin," friends are "strangers" or "enemies" or "demons," words take on peculiarly twisted meanings. He is isolated beyond reason.

Like the neurotic, the psychotic suffers from an exaggeration of normal mental processes. His disease is more massive—as if far larger parts of the brain were involved. The new element is one of total disorganization. On a small scale we are familiar with some of the psychotic's feelings. Perhaps the closest thing to schizophrenia in us is the first instant after awakening from a nightmare. The dream is still reverberating in our heads and fantasy is still real to us. We are still terrified or depressed. Then reality comes into its own, we find ourselves in familiar places and are appropriately relieved. A schizophrenic does not awaken completely and is not relieved. He lives in a dreamlike in-between state.

If schizophrenia is a caricature of confusion, paranoia is a caricature of certainty. The paranoiac has systematized his delusions so thoroughly that things fit into their places with pathological neatness. There are no ifs and maybes. Every fact, every experience and circumstance of his past and present are built ingeniously into a complex framework of ideas. This is philosophy incarnate, logic gone mad. The paranoiac is perfectly consistent and that is the mark of his insanity. He will talk rationally for hours, but one word may be enough to start him off on his obsessive theme.

Then his delusion pours out—the plot against him, the reasons for it, hints about his counterplots—in the most elaborate detail imaginable. He is a fanatic who must be watched carefully, because you never know when he will strike back at his imagined enemies. I spoke with one such patient, a middle-aged spinster who had nearly decapitated a psychiatrist three months before by rigging up a homemade guillotine over her door. The real world is not a consistent place. Those who find it so are dangerous, whether they live inside or outside of mental institutions.

Manic-depressive psychosis is a caricature of all our up-and-down tendencies. As a rule we know, or think we know, why we become depressed or elated. But many violent swings of emotion come without warning and without apparent reason (although we can create reasons as endlessly as any psychotic.) They disappear, casually after a good night's sleep, despite the fact that we continue to live the same lives with the same people. The world does not change often enough to account for the frequency of our moods, or radically enough to account for their intensity. Things are apt to be no better, and no worse, the morning after the night before.

We often call our moods irrational. Actually they are simply unexplained, and that is something else again. For relatively brief periods we are all victims of brain processes which we do not yet understand and cannot control, processes which take place whether or not we can point to definite causes. The manic-depressive shows these tendencies for all to see, uncluttered by the offering of reasons that are not reasons. His gloomy, inactive period may last two weeks and be followed by a few normal days. Then he may go to the other extreme, become intensely excited for two weeks, and swing back again as regularly as a pendulum. His moods are rhythmical, automatic, predictable and completely unrelated to current events in the outside world.

You may have heard that the difference between neurosis and psychosis is chiefly one of degree, that both conditions are part of the same process. Accumulating evidence weighs heavily against this notion. It is best to think of two completely different sets of brain diseases. A good medical parallel is the relationship between stomach ulcers and stomach cancer. Specialists believe that ulcers hardly ever lead to the development of malignant tumors, although this may happen now and then. Similarly, in the great majority of mental cases psychosis is not the last stage of an increasingly severe neurosis. It is a distinct problem in itself.

Incidentally, we have mentioned the major types of psychosis: manic-depressive conditions, schizophrenia, paranoia. But doctors rarely see them in pure form. Ninety-nine out of every hundred state-hospital inmates are mixtures of all three types. Furthermore, an individual mental patient may not stay put. He may be paranoid at one time, schizoid at another and manic-depressive later on. As one psychiatrist told me: "It isn't what they have. It's how much of each—and when."

TREATMENT BY SHOCK

Early one afternoon at Manteno I had my first chance to see electric-shock treatments being administered on an "assembly line" basis. The treatments took place in a wide corridor passing one of the men's wards. Over to one side a doctor stood near a small platform on wheels that looked like the movable stands for office typewriters, and on the platform was a compact current generator enclosed in a black cabinet.

The first patient, a young man with disheveled black hair, was lying on a bed on the other side of the corridor, his back to the electrical apparatus. He didn't know where he was or exactly what was about to happen. But he knew he had been brought there for something special, and he was obviously very frightened. His eyes had a sudden startled look as the bed he was in began rolling across the floor. The doctor had finished adjusting various dials, and had signaled that everything was checked and ready.

When the bed stopped rolling, it was next to the black cabinet. Four attendants, two on each side of the bed, stood over the patient prepared to play their role in the treatment. From this moment on, things happened swiftly. The attendants bent over and gripped the arms and legs of the patient. A nurse pressed two round metal plates simultaneously against the patient's temples, and held them there firmly as an electric current passed through his brain. He lost consciousness immediately. The current flowed for less than half a second, but that was long enough to throw him into a major convulsion and keep the attendants busy holding him on the table. Then the man—panting, sweating, exhausted and still unconscious—was taken to the ward near-by.

I watched half a dozen patients being subjected to the brief ordeal, one after the other and within half an hour. Administered under such conditions, this is a grim procedure, and psychiatrists would not be using if it they could achieve the same results less crudely. But to date this treatment, with all its limitations, has proved itself as one of the most valuable ways of breaking through the isolation of mental patients and invading the pathological privacy that is their disease. The invasion must be of the blitz variety. Gradual measures are not likely to be as effective as violent, sudden attacks on affected nerve centers in the brain.

Electric shocks have produced noteworthy results among depressed, suicidal patients at Manteno and elsewhere. On the average, a series of fifteen to twenty-five treatments improves the patient appreciably. He suffers less and can communicate with other people. He goes home and returns to his job. Even when relapses occur (an unfortunately common event), there are important benefits. Instead of being depressed continuously for eighteen months or so, he gets better in a few weeks and may not slip back for five or six months. He is at home longer and sane longer. And sometimes, for some reason, symptoms may vanish permanently. The most spectacular records are reported for women who become psychotically depressed during their change of life. Ten years ago such patients had a fifty-fifty chance of recovering after three years of suffering. Today more than 80 per cent of the group can be shocked back to sanity within three weeks.

Shock treatment is new in the sense that it has been used on a large scale only during the past decade or so. But it was tried and discarded several times in the past. In fact, something like it was recommended before the days of batteries, dynamos and electrical outlets. Patients of one Dr. Scribonius Largus, a physician of ancient Rome, received shocks for headaches and other conditions. The apparatus was a natural battery, the Mediterranean electric ray or torpedo fish which develops high-potency currents of 100 to 150 volts. According to the prescription, it was placed across the brow (although the details of how this was done are not available). The fish was made to discharge "until the patient's senses were benumbed."

What happened to the patients, or to the doctors who tried handling electric fish, is another omitted detail. But after the Romans the records are significantly silent. Modern shock treatments were inspired by two observations. Specialists in France and Germany noted that certain schizophrenics recovered as the result of a single spontaneous convulsion. About twenty years ago a Swiss investigator announced a supplementary finding, compiling statistics to show that epilepsy and schizophrenia are rarely found in the same patient. We have described how Dr. Meduna, who was living in Hungary at the time, took the next step and used drugs related to camphor to produce artificial convulsions in mental patients.

Finally, after a detour of more than eighteen hundred years, the

road leads back to Rome. In 1937 Drs. L. Bini and U. Cerletti of
the University of Rome Medical School knew that electric shocks
would also bring on convulsions, but they were worried about the
effects of large currents on the brain. Then they heard about some
"experiments" at another institution which was not directly concerned with medical progress. A local slaughterhouse was using
shocks routinely to make hogs unconscious before putting them to
death. The Italian researchers got in touch with slaughterhouse
executives, visited the plant and saw one hog get up and walk
away after receiving more than two hundred volts for ninety
seconds. Such evidence convinced them that human beings could
safely take lower voltages for a few tenths of a second, and developments since then have borne them out.

The big problem now is to find out why the treatments work.
How can electric currents, forced into the brain for a fraction of
a second, bring patients back to their senses? According to some
investigators, the answer may involve a fuller understanding of
the processes which make it possible for us to pay attention, to keep
in touch with the flow of events. We consider ourselves fairly
alert and feel we have a good grip on reality. Yet we spend most
of our waking lives in a peculiar state of detachment from the
things that are going on around us. Most of the time—about fifty-
nine minutes of every hour, on the average—you are not fully
aware of the outside world. You are busy carrying on automatic
activities like dressing, typing, driving and so on. You daydream
or read murder mysteries and other forms of fantasy.

But at least you can summon yourself to attention whenever
you want to, an ability which may be impaired in many mental
patients. When you concentrate on something, you send "alert"
signals to important nerve centers in the depths of your brain.
These centers, located in the brainstem, go into action and relay
streams of electrical nerve impulses upward to the highest center
of all. They flash signals to the cortex, the thin sheet of cells
which co-ordinates our memories and emotions and ideas. If the
alerting mechanisms in a person's brainstem are not working
properly, his ability to focus on the world about him is lost or

seriously reduced. In other words, he may be isolated from reality the way we all are in our most absent-minded moments.

Hearing an impatient voice or suddenly remembering what we forgot to do is usually enough to snap us out of our daydreams. But mental patients need an extra push. Electric shocks seem to prod nerve cells into activity and set the centers of attention going again. They may have roughly the same effect on the brainstem as the strong turn of a crank has on a stalled truck engine. Although this explanation is one of the most plausible advanced so far, it has not yet been proved. The problem remains to be settled by brain investigators. Practicing psychiatrists often treat first and discover later what it is they are doing.

Electric-shock treatments are widely used at institutions like Manteno. So is another technique, the injection of insulin in large enough doses to reduce blood sugar sharply and produce deep comas and, sometimes, convulsions. Both methods help alleviate serious troubles for medical administrators as well as patients. Manteno has overcome obstacles which still confront all too many state hospitals. In 1937 a severe typhoid epidemic from an infected deep well became a tragedy that shocked the nation. Eight years later morale again reached a low ebb. Poorly paid employees were quitting at a rate of a hundred a month, patients were consequently neglected and the newspapers made the most of it. Relatives of patients picketed the town's small bus station, shouting complaints and carrying signs describing conditions at the "Manteno Madhouse."

Today reporters on the lookout for front-page exposés would find little material for their columns. Manteno has successfully passed through its share of crises. But it has not licked the chronic, persistent problem that plagues every state hospital. It is caught in an inexorable "pincers movement." The hospital is overcrowded, having 8,000 patients or 2,900 more than it was built to house. To make matters worse, it is operating with a serious shortage of doctors.

Electric-shock and insulin treatments are an important factor in making it possible to release more than 2,500 patients a year.

But relapses occur and new patients keep coming. If these treatments did not exist, our mental institutions would start slipping back to the bedlams they were not so many years ago. State-hospital psychiatrists are forced to work under terrific pressure, because there are so many sick people waiting for help.

INVESTIGATING MADNESS

Discovering better treatments is as important as providing cleaner wards, adequately trained attendants and physicians and other highly publicized reforms. Many psychiatrists believe the next few years will see significant advances in the fight against mental disease. But they hesitate to predict the lines along which such advances will be made—and for very good reasons. Basic research is unpredictable. Important new facts often come from strange and unexpected sources. Every research project draws on the findings of many investigators at many scattered laboratories.

One of the most interesting Manteno studies involved a new treatment for a severe and bizarre mental illness. A psychiatrist led me into a small ward set aside for a special group of patients. There were five beds, five chairs and five men in the room. None of the men were moving; none of them paid any attention to us or to one another. They were grotesque statues. The only sound was a sharp, hollow clicking which I couldn't identify at first. Then I saw it was coming from a man seated in a corner, chin on hand and teeth chattering, a caricature of Rodin's "Thinker." His eyes were narrowed. His mouth was partly open as if he had just remembered something and was about to make a comment. But the comment never came.

We spoke to him several times without receiving any attention, much less an answer. I was informed that the patient, William C., hadn't said a word for more than two years. The psychiatrist took the free arm of the patient, raised it until it was pointing straight up at the ceiling and let go. The arm remained raised in its awkward position. "He'd keep it there for hours. Now you move it." I set the arm back in its former position on William's lap. It had a peculiar feeling as it moved—soft, flexible, almost boneless and muscleless. The other men were similarly inert. Two lay in bed, staring at nothing in particular, one rested on his elbow in an effeminate posture and one sat on a chair with a remote smile on his face. They were all victims of catatonia, a form of schizophrenia.

The experimental treatment for these Manteno patients was based on apparently unrelated studies I had learned about several summers ago. I was at Woods Hole, Massachusetts, on the southwestern tip of Cape Cod, which is most widely known as the place where vacationers catch the steamer for Martha's Vineyard and Nantucket. But Woods Hole is also the site of the Marine Biological Laboratory, the nation's summertime center for research in the life sciences. Here Dr. David Nachmansohn and his colleagues, of Columbia University's College of Physicians and Surgeons, were studying basic mechanisms responsible for electrical signals relayed back and forth along the fibers of the brain and nervous system.

A good deal has been written about electrical impulses in the brain, impulses whose subtle patterns determine our ideas, emotions and actions. But how are they produced? We know that a resting or inactive nerve fiber is loaded and ready to flash messages. There is a positive electrical charge on its surface. If the charge changes from positive to negative at any point, a kind of electrical "hole" is produced. Electricity from the nearby fiber surface promptly flows into the hole, filling it but also creating a new hole. The new hole, in turn, is filled from the next neighboring region and so on down the full length of the fiber. Thus, the nerve impulse travels along and around the fiber like a smoke ring and transforms it into a living fuse. The fastest impulses move at speeds of more than five miles a minute.

The Columbia University group had found that highly complex chemical reactions account for these impulses. There are no batteries with metal plates in the nervous system, and no armatures or generators. Nature does the whole thing by shuttling electrically charged particles back and forth through the pores in the membranes that sheathe nerve fibers. Part of the process involves two substances known as ACh and ChE (short for acetylcholine and cholinesterase, respectively). When you are scared or angry ChE, a potent chemical stimulant, breaks down billions of ACh molecules in certain nerves leading to your heart. This mass effect takes place in a few thousandths of a second. It sets things stirring among charged particles around the nerves, an electrical impulse is produced and your heart responds by beating faster.

What happens when there's too little ChE or none at all? The answer to this question involves an imaginary trip from Woods Hole to the closely guarded laboratories of the Army's Chemical Warfare Service at Edgewood Arsenal in Maryland. After the war certain facts were released about a new poison gas that in extremely small quantities could produce paralysis and death. Other nations also worked on this substance. It was the "nerve gas" which, according to rumor, the Nazis used at Liége in Belgium as part of their drive to flank the Maginot Line. It paralyzes by effectively destroying ChE and depressing the electrical activity of vital nerves.

The scene shifts overseas to the Middlesex Hospital in London. Two years ago a young surgeon, Dr. Stephen Sherwood, began fitting the facts together into a theory. He knew about the nerve-gas research and suggested that the paralyzing stupor of catatonia might result from a lack or shortage of the nerve "sparkplug," ChE. Specifically, the trouble might lie in a tiny structure near the hypothalamus which helps co-ordinate the expression of emotion and supply us with our nervous energy and drive.

Catatonic patients might be driven out of their lethargy if extra amounts of ChE were somehow brought into this critical region. After some preliminary experiments in England, Dr. Sherwood visited the United States and Manteno. Things started humming. Working together with Manteno and University of Illinois investigators, he had a chance to put his theory to the test systematically. He used ChE extracted from the shock-producing tissues of *Electrophorus electricus,* the electric eel, and supplied by Dr. Nachmansohn who had been conducting basic nerve-chemistry studies for years in New York and Woods Hole. The material came in the form of a water-clear, gluey liquid.

William C. was the first American patient to receive the new treatment. Two small burr holes were drilled in the front part of his skull, one on each side of the midline. A slender hypodermic needle was inserted through each hole to a depth of about an inch and a half, until its tip entered one of the brain's ventricles or fluid-filled cavities, and ChE was injected into the cavity. The patient's response was rapid and spectacular. Within a few minutes you could see his greasy, blue-gray skin, a typical sign of catatonia, changing to a pink normal color.

His eyes lost their glassy stare. Suddenly he began paying attention to things around him, especially when he thought people weren't looking. At dinner that evening, about two hours after the injections, the patient spoke for the first time in some two years. This would have been a better story if he'd made some significant or particularly quotable statement. But in real life the breaking of long silences, like a person's last words, is seldom dramatic. A doctor pointed to an item on the dinner tray and William said: "Cabbage." The word was uttered slowly in a low sepulchral tone which reminded the doctor of the voice announcing the mystery broadcast "Inner Sanctum." Later he began using full sentences. He confessed to eating most of another patient's meal, and told Dr. Sherwood he was tired and wanted some sleep.

William is one of a dozen patients treated to date. Improvements have been marked, but the change lasts only about ten days on the average. No one knows how many injections may be needed to bring permanent relief—and sufficient ChE isn't yet available for large-scale tests. The minute amount Dr. Sherwood obtained, less than a fifth of an ounce, cost several thousand dollars to produce and represents the extract from a whole flotilla of electric eels. Moreover, unpublished studies indicate that human ChE from red blood cells is far more potent than the eel variety.

But whatever the results of continuing research along these lines may be, psychiatrists feel that such treatments—treatments with nerve medicines and drugs—represent one of the most promising approaches to the problem of mental disease. Many other projects are under way at Manteno. New drugs are being screened to curb epilepsy, relieve anxiety and emotional stress and achieve the results of shock treatment without producing convulsions. New techniques are being evolved for exploring the detailed anatomy of the brain and advancing experimental surgery. If we are ever to conquer mental disease, however, Manteno and all state hospitals must have the chance to do a great deal more research.

"There's something a bit mad about the way we investigate madness," one administrator told me. "Most of our patients are suffering in mental institutions isolated miles out in the country —and most researchers are busy working somewhere else, at medical centers in big cities." He believes that only one out of every twenty state hospitals has the people, the budget or the will needed to carry on a first-rate research program, and I have heard even more pessimistic estimates. Manteno is a notable exception to the general rule.

14

THE RISE OF PSYCHOSURGERY

Psychosurgery, operations for the treatment of mental patients, is something relatively new in psychiatry. The field has enjoyed a spectacular boom during the past decade or so. Before that surgeons generally hesitated to apply their craft to psychiatric disorders of the brain. For one thing, the predominant feeling of the times used to be that by far the most important factor in mental disease was emotional conflict, shocks suffered in early childhood, escape from reality. Less popular was the notion that physical causes—for example, faulty genes or gland ailments—could be just as upsetting and affect the brain just as dramatically as psychological causes. Surgeons also hesitated, because there was not enough evidence from animal experiments to justify preliminary clinical trials.

Frontal lobotomy, literally "cutting away," was the first operation used extensively for mental disease. It effectively separates part of the cortex from the rest of the brain and has been used on many more mental patients than all other operations together. In this case, however, wide use does not imply wide agreement among surgeons as to its usefulness. You can hear surgeons arguing about its merits and drawbacks even today, after thousands of patients have been treated. Titles of popular articles reflect the optimism of the early days: "Cutting Out Cares," "Sanity Restored by Surgery," "Brain Surgery Banishes Worry." More recent articles indicate that caution may follow, as well as precede, experience: "The Operation of Last Resort," "Lobotomy—Savior or Destroyer?"

What happened to bring about the change in tone? Why was frontal lobotomy once called "Operation Zombie"? What are some of its more dramatic failures—and its real and often striking benefits? How does it work? Enough information has accumulated to permit fairly definite answers to such questions, and the problems to be discussed feature case histories based on interviews and stenographic records. Later we will describe some of the many new operating techniques being explored in preliminary tests. The techniques are those which leading investigators believe may be the basis of psychosurgery in the future.

CORINNE'S STORY

A psychiatrist and I were walking across the neatly trimmed front lawn of the Connecticut State Hospital in Middletown. Our path led toward a long red-brick building, one of the mental wards. As we came closer, patients shouted at us from a wire-enclosed porch. We entered the building, passed through a series of zigzagging corridors and stopped at a locked door. The psychiatrist opened the door with his key, and a nurse led us along another corridor to another door. I followed them into the room.

Corinne, a thirty-two-year-old schizophrenic, was sitting tensely in a chair. She moved her hands continually, gesticulating to herself, twisting her thumbs and fingers. Her right foot pounded a persistent rhythm on the floor. "Can we talk with you, Corinne?" the psychiatrist asked. She didn't answer or look at us.

"How do you feel today?" Still no answer.

"What's the matter?" The psychiatrist bent over, to shake her shoulder gently.

Suddenly Corinne lifted her head and screamed a frightening "Go away!" We didn't go away, and Corinne finally answered our questions. She usually spoke in a flat, emotionless voice. But from time to time, when she told us about imagined enemies, she became terrified and panicky.

"He's under the floor now. He follows me all over, under the floor. He hates me. He keeps calling me bad names."

"Who hates you?"

"Major Brown. I hear him under the floor. I can hear him breathing. He wants to punish me. Yesterday he tried to cut me with a piece of broken glass."

"What does Major Brown say to you."

"I couldn't tell you that. They're bad words. He tells me: 'There's a devil in you—you're dirty as sin.' He has a machine that sends out electrical waves that burn my skin. I want to get out of here. This isn't a hospital. The people here are just pretending to be sick."

Corinne began screaming again. She shouted insults at us. She said we were Major Brown's agents sent to spy on her. By the time we started walking to the door, she had calmed down. As I left the room, I could hear her foot pounding the floor as it had when we entered.

Later I read Corinne's case record. She had been brought up near a small village near Hartford. Her parents remember her as a somewhat moody, but not alarmingly moody, child who did well at school. She began to change noticeably at the age of sixteen or seventeen. She would sit in the living room, clasping and unclasping her hands, and then jump up suddenly and shake her head in a puzzled manner. She told her mother that she felt something terrible was about to happen, that she'd done something wrong and was going to suffer for it.

These spells became more frequent and more intense. One night Corinne rushed out of her bedroom, shouting that "Major Brown" was trying to poison her (this was the first time she had mentioned the name of her imaginary tormentor). She ran downstairs and out of the house before her family could stop her. Next morning the police found her four miles away, cowering near a large tree. That was in 1942. She had been living with her nightmare ever since.

Several weeks later I saw Corinne again, this time on the operating table. A surgeon had already started operating on her brain. Two "buttonholes" of bone, each about the size of a half dollar, had been removed from the top of her head exposing the pinkish-gray surface of the brain. One hole was located on the left front part of the skull, the other on the right.

The surgeon was working at the right-hand opening. He inserted a narrow steel needle through the hole at a forward angle so that it passed slowly through the top layer of gray matter and down into the white matter underneath. The needle stopped when it made gentle contact with the upper part of the bony shelf that juts out over the eye. This probe served as a guide for a spatula, a blunt two-edged knife which looks something like the tool used to spread paint.

Looking down into a wedge-shaped cleft, the surgeon pushed the spatula along the plane of the needle to a depth of more than two inches. Then he moved the knife through a side-to-side arc, cutting a thin path across the white matter. He still had to cut an inch deeper, and this step was accomplished with a special knife marked off in millimeters. The "calibrated" spatula was lowered until it touched the bony shelf, raised a fraction of an inch, and swung through another arc.

Corinne was conscious throughout the entire fifty-minute operation, having received a local anesthetic only (the brain feels no pain). Up to this stage of the surgery she was as nervous as she had been during my first visit. She was breathing heavily and grasping the edge of the table with trembling fingers. Her hands were cold and white.

But a dramatic change took place after the surgeon performed the same incisions through the left-hand buttonhole. As soon as the second knife had completed its deepest cut, the muscles in Corinne's arms and legs all relaxed at once. She made no sound, but her entire body seemed to heave a sigh of relief. Now she was breathing slowly. She released her desperate hold on the edge of the table, and color began returning to her hands.

I saw Corinne for the last time about a week after her operation. She looked up as we came into the room, but she didn't say anything until the psychiatrist greeted her and asked her how she was feeling. "I'm much better, doctor. I think the hospital is good for me.

My hands are nice and warm now. Who's that with you? A writer? There's a lot to write about in this place."

Corinne answered questions in a cheerful and somewhat languid voice, without much expression on her face. She would speak if spoken to, but acted as if it was too much trouble to keep the conversation going. Her fears had vanished completely—so completely, in fact, that I assumed she no longer had her hallucinations. Then the psychiatrist asked, "Where is Major Brown?"

"Oh, he's here somewhere under the floor."

"Does he still speak to you?"

"Yes."

"What does he say?"

"He tells me I'm bad and calls me names. Things like that."

"Do the voices frighten you?"

"No, doctor."

Although Corinne continued to hear Major Brown's voice for a week after her operation, it didn't bother her. A few days later the voice stopped entirely. But she wasn't yet ready for the loss of her illusions, so she explained that her ears were stopped up. Still later, the patient told a nurse that the Major had gone away probably for good. The final stage came one afternoon when Corinne said: "Of course, I can't hear voices. That's silly—you don't hear voices under the floor."

Corinne will never be completely sane. She will find it difficult to concentrate on anything for more than a short period. She will be less active physically. She will be less inhibited than most of us, and her outspoken remarks may shock or insult unwarned visitors. But the operation has also produced marked and beneficial changes. Corinne is back with her family and she has improved sufficiently to help around the house. Even more important, the demons that tormented her are not likely to return. Major Brown and her voices have disappeared together.

THE FIRST PSYCHOSURGEONS

Corinne's case resembles those of many mental patients who have had frontal lobotomies. Later we will be discussing facts and theories about how such operations work. But first it may be helpful to go into the early experiments that led to present-day techniques. Frontal lobotomy is one of the most important developments in the history of psychiatry. Its results are not always predictable, but the very fact that it *has* definite and permanent results is significant. The past has been an unspectacular record of supersitions, fads and knowledge acquired at a snail's pace.

Centuries ago Indians in the highlands of Peru, like prehistoric cave-dwellers, knew where to look for their demons. They made holes in the skulls of demented persons. The practice may have helped in some cases, presumably by scaring patients into their wits (severe physical shock has been known to restore sanity, at least temporarily). After that, surgery for insanity circumnavigated the entire body before returning to the brain. The Greeks, anticipating Freud, concentrated on the sex organs—castration was recommended for men, removal of the ovaries for women. In more recent times treatment included removal of the thyroid gland, tonsils, appendix, teeth, colon or other organs. A few halfhearted attempts to operate on the brain were not followed up, mainly because few surgeons dared to explore the uncharted pathways of the cerebral jungle.

Modern psychosurgery has been practiced for less than fifteen years on a large scale. But its beginnings can be traced to the summer of 1933. A research team at Johns Hopkins had been studying the common cold and no longer needed some of its experimental animals. One of the animals, a six-year-old chimpanzee named Becky, was spoken for by Drs. John Fulton and Carlyle Jacobsen of Yale University's physiology laboratory. The New Haven scientists were investigating the frontal lobes and decided to put the chimpanzee through an elaborate set of intelligence tests.

Becky was "of a volatile temperament, loving, affectionate and highly dependent on the reassurance that came to her from human company." For the most part, she co-operated beautifully. Although she wasn't very bright, her efforts to reach food with sticks were a model of simian patience. But one type of test in particular ruffled her normally agreeable disposition. Becky watched curiously as a piece of food was placed under one of two identical cups. Then a sliding panel blocked her view of the cups and she was supposed to wait until the panel was removed.

The cups weren't moved during the "blind" interval. Becky simply had to remember which of them contained the food. Her reward for passing the test was a blue poker chip that could be inserted into a special food-delivering "Chimpomat." This sort of test was too much for the chimpanzee's memory span. After making a few mistakes, she would scream with rage, roll on the floor and beat her chest. Eventually she developed a full-fledged mental disorder.

To treat Becky's condition, Drs. Fulton and Jacobsen removed more than an ounce of her frontal lobes. After the operation, Becky didn't do any better in the tests, or any worse. But she didn't care. When she made a mistake, she simply shrugged her shoulders and went on to something else. According to the scientists' report, "It was as if the animal had joined the happiness cult of the Elder Micheaux and had placed its burdens in the Lord."

These results were announced in 1935 at the London meeting of the International Neurological Congress. In the audience was Dr. Egas Moniz of Lisbon who for several years had been studying the possibility of surgery for mental disease. Although he believed that a properly designed operation would bring relief, he couldn't convince some of his colleagues. The psychiatrist rushed up to Dr. Fulton after the announcement and described his plans for the future. He felt that Becky's case would provide the evidence needed to obtain permission for trials on human beings.

The hunch turned out to be correct. Within three months Dr. Moniz and his associates had operated on twenty cases. Instead of cutting across brain tissue, they actually removed portions of white matter, four to six small cores from each side of the brain. Preliminary results were encouraging. Seven patients seemed to have recovered and seven improved; six patients were not benefited. If Dr. Moniz had been able to carry out his plans, things would have proceeded with due scientific caution from this stage on. His plans were to perform no further operations—until he had followed his patients for at least five years and was more certain of its long-term effects. He wanted to go slow.

But Dr. Moniz had not counted on the enthusiasm of some of his professional brethren across the Atlantic Ocean. The first specialists to read about his work, and do something about it, were Drs. Walter Freeman and James W. Watts of George Washington University in Washington, D.C. They promptly communicated with the Portuguese investigator, learned further details about his technique, and tried it on a fifty-nine-year-old bookkeeper who had been deeply depressed for a year and a half. In subsequent cases they departed from the Moniz method of removing tissue cores, and developed the forerunner of modern lobotomies in which brain tissue is cut but left in place.

Drs. Freeman and Watts played a major part in selling psychosurgery to American psychiatrists and surgeons. By 1942 they had published a book describing operations on more than seventy-five patients. Furthermore, they co-operated with Waldemar Kaempffert, science editor of the *New York Times,* by furnishing information for an article that appeared in the *Saturday Evening Post.* Some of the representatives of organized medicine were outraged by what they considered a breach of medical ethics. But the upshot was that an increasing number of lobotomies were performed during and after the war. In 1949 Dr. Moniz was awarded a Nobel Prize for his pioneer studies.

To date an estimated fifty thousand patients throughout the world have had frontal lobotomies, half in the United States and half abroad. The results are similar to those announced in Dr. Moniz's original paper. About a third of all patients treated are not benefited at all, while an equal proportion are improved but still have to be kept in hospitals. The remaining third can return to their homes—some to their former jobs and a normal life, others to limited activities at home.

"It Stopped the Tension"

How does frontal lobotomy work, when it works? What happens when a patient's hallucinations stop as if turned off by a switch?

While new theories help answer these questions, the full story awaits further research. The operation is still more art than science. The surgeon's knife is guided by visible features of the cerebral landscape—familiar ridges, convolutions and blood vessels. But most of the intimate details of the underlying structures are un-charted territory, and often the knife that cuts through them must blaze new trails instead of following old ones.

Many investigators have studied what goes on when the final cut is made in the operating room. Some years ago Dr. Benjamin Simon, clinical director of the Connecticut State Hospital, reported a unique record of a man's feelings during lobotomy. Like most cases, the patient was a schizophrenic and was conscious through-out the operation. The following is a transcript of his answers to Dr. Simon's questions as a surgeon cut into his brain:

"Are you feeling any pain?"

"No, doctor."

"What do you think of all this? What are they doing to you?"

"Well, he is doing some kind of operation on my head."

"What do you think it will do for you?"

"I want to be able to go back to work."

"Why can't you do that now?"

"I don't know. There's something the matter with my mind— oh, I felt something then!" (The surgeon had just completed his final cut in the patient's frontal lobes.)

"What did you feel? Was it pain?"

"No, it didn't hurt. It did something to the pressure."

"What do you mean by that?"

"It stopped the tension." At this point the patient became drowsy and fell asleep, muttering something about "the doctor drilling my worries away."

This sort of operation has its first and most direct effect on two nerve centers. It involves the cortex, the highest center of all, and the thalamus, the brain's largest relay station. A thick cable of many millions of nerve fibers passes up into the brain, carrying a variety of sensations including heat, cold, vision and hearing. In the thalamus the fibers of this cable are sorted out into smaller bundles which pass upward, each headed for its particular area, its "map," on the curving surface of the cortex. In other words, a cable enters the thalamus from the bottom, and a series of smaller nerve bundles branch out from the top like the stem of a plant.

We know what messages many of these bundles carry. One bundle passes up to the cortex at the back of the brain; if it is cut, we cannot see. Another bundle of fibers, which reaches areas at the sides of the head, transmits auditory signals and we become deaf if it is severed. But many ascending fibers can be traced to the front of the cortex, the areas beneath the forehead, and the functions of this region are not clearly understood. Even more fibers pass downward to the thalamus, so that the total for ascending and descending traffic is about ten million. The frontal regions of the cortex were once called "silent areas." They could be stimulated and injured without producing any effects, at least, without producing effects which early investigators could find.

Today we know that the silent areas are anything but silent. They are part of the brain's "emoting" system. Electrical nerve messages streaming to these regions from the thalamus and lower centers are somehow translated into feelings. The feelings come and go, and are rarely intense enough to inspire or shake us. In mental disease, however, they may be exceedingly intense and persistent. This is another way of saying that certain electrical signals are abnormally large and keep coming. In a successful frontal lobotomy feelings of anxiety, of panic and terror, stop when fibers carrying the signals are severed.

There are various forms of lobotomy, and all of them involve cutting nerve-fiber cables running to the front part of the cortex. Incidentally, in another type of operation the cables are cut at the upper end; small pieces of cortex are removed. Also, surgeons may operate directly at the depths of the brain, using a special needle to get at cells in the thalamus (this procedure is described in the next chapter). But whatever the technique, results on patients are comparable.

The patient's ideas can be affected as dramatically as his emotions. At the onset of his illness a victim of schizophrenia may experience only a vague feeling of impending doom. He may sense

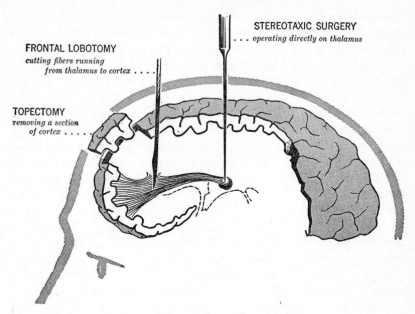

STEREOTAXIC SURGERY
. . . operating directly on thalamus

FRONTAL LOBOTOMY
*cutting fibers running
from thalamus to cortex . . . .*

TOPECTOMY
*removing a section
of cortex . . . . .*

Some Types of Psychosurgery

that his fears are irrational. But they are real and he seeks to explain them logically and consistently. He builds an intellectual framework to contain his feelings. He creates an elaborate myth, step by step—complete with Major Browns, plots and counterplots. Later a surgeon comes along and cuts thalamus-to-cortex fibers, and the myths fade together with the feelings that inspire them. Something of this sort happened when Corinne gradually realized that Major Brown and his agents had never existed.

Lobotomy produces other changes. The frontal areas of the cortex are connected with centers that regulate such reflexes as breathing, heart and pulse rates, dilation of the pupil of the eye and tension of the muscles. Surgery may bring about a fall in blood pressure. Patients breathe more slowly, tire easily and are even more reluctant than the rest of us to get up and go to work. Such observations confirm anatomical findings that the brain is an integrated unit. Its centers are interconnected, and you cannot sever important fibers without affecting many things together—ideas, emotions, reflexes, general bodily activity. The intensity of living is lowered, as abruptly as if you turned down the volume control of a blaring radio.

Lobotomy is not a cure in any basic sense. It treats symptoms, and there is no reason to believe that the knife stops once and for all the electrical impulses which were the patient's fears. What happens is that they never reach his cortex and his mind may be at peace. If we knew where the impulses were generated and the reason that certain deep-lying nerve cells send persistent messages, mental disease would be less of a mystery. Some clues will be discussed later. At this point we will only mention one observation contributed by surgeons who are seeing many more mentally ill brains than they did before the coming of psychosurgery.

Their unpublished comments indicate that schizophrenic brains are often slightly shrunken. The convolutions are broader than usual. The ridges are narrower and jut out more prominently. The entire organ has a yellowish cast and feels hard and rubbery. The significance of these common changes is that they closely resemble changes seen in the brains of persons who have died from such virus ailments as encephalitis or sleeping sickness. Of course, this does not mean that schizophrenia is caused by submicroscopic organisms. It merely indicates that many patients are suffering from abnormal processes which affect the brain in much the same way as viruses.

LIFE AFTER LOBOTOMY

Psychosurgery will continue to be used in the treatment of mental illness, at least until we know more about causes. But it must be used carefully. When the surgeon kills nerve cells in the brain, he is "playing for keeps." As pointed out before, the nerve cells you are born with must do for a lifetime and are never replaced. So lobotomy should not be tried indiscriminately. It produces personality changes which are difficult to measure and may leave the patient happier but less human. Although I.Q. scores and memory do not seem to be significantly affected, other faculties may undergo permanent alterations.

Every person must be somewhat obsessed to achieve his goal in life. A certain amount of tension and drive is socially acceptable and, in some communities, desirable. In fact, man alone of all species seems to have built into his nervous system something which keeps him on the go exploring, competing, learning, theorizing. Most lobotomized patients have lost the ability (or desire?) to keep up with the Joneses or seek out new experiences. They live almost completely in the present and their capacity for caring is impaired. The future is of little concern, so they do not plan for the future or look ahead—or worry or fear. This is strong evidence that nerve cells in the frontal cortex are important in enabling us to plan and predict.

A few years ago British surgeons operated on an internationally famous bridge player, who still plays a good game with his friends. He still knows what to do and why. But he isn't up to the demands of tournament play, because he doesn't mind going down a trick or two. In a few cases, there are more serious consequences. Dr. Freeman tells the story of a patient who saw a red box on the wall of a hospital corridor, and proceeded to pull the chain that hung from it. After clanging fire alarms had been stilled, he admitted knowing what the box was for and what would happen. But he didn't bother to think further ahead: "Now that I have done it, I see that I shouldn't. . . . But before I did it I couldn't tell whether or not it would be the right thing to do."

Lobotomy produced an unexpected change in another patient, a lawyer. Before his operation, the man would go off on violent binges every three months or so. He drank heavily and shattered chairs, tables and glasses at various bars (he never attacked people). It wasn't until the sober aftermath, however, that he really began to suffer from gloomy periods of guilt and remorse. He asked a surgeon to operate on his brain after an attempt at suicide that almost succeeded. The operation worked—in a fashion. The lawyer still went on binges. He still drank heavily and still smashed furniture. But he no longer felt guilty about it.

In the early days a few patients lost the capacity to do much more than breathe and swallow. Some of them curled up into the fetal position like victims of advanced syphilis of the brain. Others stared vacantly and hardly moved. These results were relatively rare, but they inspired the grim nickname "Operation Zombie." Today such cases are practically unknown, because most operations performed are far less extensive. It is estimated that the number of fibers cut is about a tenth of the total cut fifteen years ago. But there is always a risk which must be weighed by a team of trained specialists. Incidentally, it seems the risk is too great for the conservative representatives of organized medicine in the Soviet Union. Partly because of an unspecified number of unsuccessful cases, lobotomy has been officially and completely banned as "nihilistic in outlook," "unsoviet in its approach to the patient," "monstrously cruel" and "disintegrative."

It is true that some Soviet surgeons, like some American surgeons, have performed lobotomies indiscriminately. Banning the treatment by law, however, has denied help to an appreciable proportion of Soviet mental patients and retarded further progress. Results may be most favorable if the operation is confined to severely afflicted psychotic patients who are suffering and who have not been benefited by less radical measures. Not long ago physicians at the Harvard Medical School and the Boston Psychopathic Hospital reported a study of one hundred patients five years after their operations. As usual, about two thirds of the group were improved. Twenty-nine patients "were earning a salary and their performance apparently satisfied their employers. If engaged as housewives, they were working full time and satisfactorily, so far as their relatives were concerned."

Such records are particularly significant when you consider how much mental patients may suffer. Think back to the most terrifying and deeply disturbing experience in your life. Now imagine living through equally intense emotions for ten years or more with little relief—and you may have some idea of why brain specialists recommend lobotomy for selected patients. Lobotomy is certainly not the last word in psychosurgery, as we shall see shortly. But it represents a major development in psychiatric research as well as treatment. The exploration of the frontal cortex of man has just begun.

15

BRAIN OPERATIONS WITH NEEDLES

I<small>T WAS</small> 10:35 A.M. in Operating Room No. 5 of Philadelphia's Temple University Hospital. The crucial part of the surgery was about to begin. I had seen the patient two days before, a schizophrenic boy only seventeen years old and the son of a Philadelphia lawyer. Glowering and suspicious, he had narrowed his eyes and asked me what I was doing in the room. Why was I standing near the window? Was I trying to get away? He frequently became violent, and attendants had watched him carefully.

Now, anesthetized and at peace with the world, the boy was propped up on the operating table, half sitting and half reclining under large surgical spotlights. His head was inside a "cage," a strange-looking piece of apparatus shaped something like a section of the Jungle Gyms in children's playgrounds. It consisted of aluminum rods built into a cubical frame. The square base of the cage had been fastened around the boy's head the way you fasten a support to the bottom of a Christmas tree. Four rubber-cushioned pins were screwed against the back of his head and his temples. Other special devices designed to hold the cage exactly in place included ear bars, a headrest and a ring resting on the scalp.

A hollow needle, held by clamps, pointed straight down toward the top of the boy's skull. Mounted on a sliding carriage, it could be moved in any of three planes—forward and backward, side to side, up and down. A surgeon turned two knobs, bringing the needle back and sideways until it stopped above a hole that had already been drilled through the left side of the skull. Then he turned another knob and the needle slowly moved down into the brain of the patient, coming to rest at a depth of exactly sixty-two millimeters (nearly two and a half inches).

Now the surgeon was ready to operate by "remote control," to work on a nerve center he couldn't even see. He flipped a switch, which ran down through the hollow needle and stuck out from the side near the bottom. The current flowed a minute, long enough to "electrocute" a group of nerve cells which occupies a volume smaller than that of the head of a match. After rotating the needle and destroying other tiny regions, the surgeon repeated the same procedure in the right side of the boy's brain. The main job was finished. It had taken about an hour and fifteen minutes.

SURGERY AT THE DEPTHS

The new operation goes by a new name—a name, by the way, that you may be hearing a good deal in the future. The cage that holds the needle in precise position and helps move it into the depths of the brain is known as a "stereotaxic" device, literally an instrument for making arrangements or adjustments in space. Surgery involving the instrument is known as "stereotaxic" surgery. The apparatus has been a standby in brain operations on animals for nearly half a century, but no one dared to try it on human beings until about six years ago.

The medical researcher who started the whole thing, Dr. Ernest Spiegel of the Temple University Medical School, had arranged for me to watch the boy being treated for mental disease. In fact, the instrument had first been used in Operating Room No. 5 by Dr. Henry Wycis who was performing the operation I saw. The surgeon still remembers their early plans and the conversation that led to the new procedure. It took place seven years ago during luncheon at the medical school and Dr. Spiegel was commenting on another operation, frontal lobotomy.

This operation is the first ever used on a large scale for mental patients. A bundle of nerves ascends from the thalamus, the important center which serves as a relay station for nerve impulses and is buried inside the brain. The bundle breaks into a "spray" of millions of individual fibers as it rises. Many of the fibers end in the front part of the cortex, the sheet of gray matter which covers the surface of the brain. Somehow the electrical messages that circulate in these fibers represent the anxieties, panics and despair of certain forms of mental disease. We know this, because when some of the fibers are cut—at some point between the cortex and the deep-seated thalamus from which they arise—such feelings may be alleviated or disappear entirely.

Frontal lobotomy is designed to make that in-between cut. When Dr. Spiegel was discussing this operation, in 1947, it was being used on more and more patients in the United States and abroad. It had already been performed on thousands of patients, sometimes with spectacular results, and investigators in many laboratories were studying cases to learn more about how and why the procedure works. For one thing, they studied the exact anatomical changes that followed the surgery. Think of the bundle of nerves coming up from the thalamus as the closely wound wire cable of a power line. We can then obtain a rough picture of the nerve fibers that spread out from the bundle to make their connections with the cortex-dome above. They can be compared to the "frayed" ends of a cable which has been unraveled into a kind of tuft.

The surgeon swings his blunt-edge knife or spatula across this tuft, severing a good many of the fibers that branch out and up to the cortex. Studies indicate what happens to each severed fiber. The part ahead of the cut, the threadlike extension that ends in the cortex, slowly dissolves away and is ultimately discarded along with other body wastes. The same thing happens to the part behind the cut, which degenerates backward down into and through the nerve bundle, as well as forward toward the cortex. Special dye stains make it possible to trace the process all the way back to the thalamus. These facts hinted at another approach to the general problem of interrupting selected pathways from thalamus to cortex.

Dr. Spiegel suggested an important change of technique. Instead of cutting the fibers in the middle, "trimming branches" as it were, it might be possible to go directly to the roots. The idea was not to use a sweeping cut across many diverging fibers, but to produce a precise pin-point injury at a specific site in the thalamus. In other words, locate the tiny injury at the exact source of the fibers. Such a procedure is somewhat analogous to damming a river at its headwaters or, in case of electrical trouble at home, shutting off the main switch in the cellar instead of fooling around with live wires upstairs. The surgery could be done with the aid of a stereotaxic instrument.

This sort of operation would have certain advantages. In frontal lobotomy the spatula enters through an opening drilled in the skull and, using that opening as a pivot point, it may swing through an arc of 60 degrees or more as it cuts across fibers. But the blade also destroys other fiber systems that lie in its path. It cuts some of the other fibers which form a maze of interlacings within the white matter underlying the gray cortex (the whole thing is something like a network of fine wires imbedded in Jello). No matter how careful the surgeon is, he cannot possibly avoid doing some damage over and above that strictly necessary to produce beneficial results.

Lowering a slender needle, however, is something else again. There is no sweeping action. The tip of the needle moves straight down as it is guided to a selected part of the thalamus, a region smaller than the nail of your little finger. It injures relatively little tissue on the way down, and does the greatest part of its damage right on the spot. This is one of the obvious and spectacular advantages of stereotaxic surgery—and one of the reasons the needle is being used to an increasing extent. The technique also raises extremely tricky problems of its own which are still being studied and have not yet been completely solved. But before going into the difficulties, we might give some indications of the bright side of the story, the results that show the difficulties are worth overcoming.

Brain cells, unlike cells of all other body tissues, are not replaced when they die. The ones you have now are as old as you are, and they will have to do as long as you live. This means that once brain tissue is destroyed, accidentally or surgically, it is gone forever.

Since the surgeon testing new procedures for mental illness cannot undo what he has done, he should—and usually does—operate on restricted regions of the brain, at least to start with. In other words, caution dictates that too little rather than too much tissue should be affected.

Drs. Spiegel and Wycis follow this policy to the letter. Lowering the needle so that the tip comes to rest in selected parts of the thalamus, they destroy nerve cells in a volume of brain tissue no larger than the end of a pencil. They interrupt the flow of impulses in nerve fibers which, when they reach the highest levels of the brain, are translated into fears and rages and tensions. Among the patients was a schizophrenic housewife who had twice attempted suicide, having failed to respond to electric-shock treatments. After surgery she returned to her children and spoke back to a nagging husband for the first time in years, presumably a sign of improved adjustment.

I heard about an even more successful case during a recent visit to Philadelphia. Dr. Wycis had just seen a man he had treated more than five years ago. Before his operation the patient, a foreman in a textile factory, had been growing more and more quick-tempered and suspicious. He finally lost his job after a fight with one of the men in his gang. "Now he's back at work," the surgeon told me, "and his employer tells me he's doing wonderfully. He doesn't lose his temper and has a pleasant personality—we made him pleasant." In all, Dr. Wycis has performed about 150 stereotaxic operations for schizophrenic and other psychiatric disorders.

Records reveal that the operations produce roughly the same results as frontal lobotomy. About one third of the patients are not benefited, one third show slight improvement and one third became much better. But as had been expected, one of the greatest differences between the two procedures is that the stereotaxic method does less damage to the brain. In every brain operation surgeons must be careful to avoid damage to tiny blood vessels, since bleeding may destroy brain tissue. Scars forming on the brain's surface may irritate neighboring cells. The result may be so-called epileptic discharges. Reports indicate that 5 per cent, or more, of patients undergoing frontal lobotomy suffer from convulsions of some sort. But such attacks are practically eliminated in the new technique.

HITTING THE TARGET

Stereotaxic surgery thus can be rated as a safer operation, at least from one point of view. The needle does little damage as it passes down into the tissues of the brain, pushing fibers aside like a knitting needle moving through a ball of loose yarn. But this is merely the most favorable part of the story. The procedure is still definitely on the experimental side, because it introduces some serious problems of its own. The surgeon is "flying blind." He is moving the tip of the needle, sight unseen, through a subtle and complex organ whose workings are only incompletely understood. If the probe goes even slightly off course, the patient's personality may be altered—radically, unpredictably and sometimes irrevocably.

Tests on monkeys indicate what might happen in case of a small error. A tiny injury made at a carefully selected site in the upper end of the brainstem produces almost complete lack of movement. Experimental animals gaze fixedly into space and sit upright, only blinking now and then and changing position slightly. In other animals a tiny injury at a different site may produce just the opposite effect. Monkeys become abnormally restless and jump about in a frenzy of uncontrollable activity. The main point is that the two sites may be less than an eighth of an inch apart, that a shift equivalent to the width of a safety match can produce a spectacular change in personality. Among human beings brainstem damage may cause a tremendous increase in laughter and sexual activity, together with a loss of appetite for food. Patients with damage in a near-by region of the brainstem may not laugh at all and have no interest in sex—but they eat eight or nine square meals a day!

In no other type of surgery is the placing of a cut or damage zone of more critical importance. Stereotaxic operations call for a degree of precision hitherto unknown in brain surgery. As has already been pointed out, nerve cells in the brain are not replaced once they are killed. The damage is often irreversible. Severed brain fibers will never repair themselves, and there is no way of splicing the ends together. The tip of the needle can be regarded as a guided missile of a sort, a missile steered by remote control toward an invisible target buried in a mass of nerve tissue.

For example, here is the general problem that confronted Dr. Wycis when he operated on the textile-plant foreman. He was aiming in the direction of a nerve center, the thalamus. To be a bit more exact, he was aiming at a particular nucleus or clump of nerve cells within that center, a target no bigger than an aspirin tablet. But only a part of the target was to be destroyed, about a third of the total mass. This sort of surgery requires pin-point accuracy. Measurements are made in millimeters—twenty-fifths of an inch—and a few millimeters either way may make all the difference as far as the success or failure of the operation is concerned.

Stereotaxic instruments are high-precision instruments. The original model was built in 1908 by Dr. Robert H. Clarke, an American investigator working in the laboratory of a London surgeon, Victor Horsley. The basic design principles have not changed appreciably since then. Dr. Clarke, who had an amazing mechanical sense, recognized the chief problems confronting designers today. The surgeon must be able to bring the needle to an exact site in the brain. Also, it must remain there throughout the operation. Those requirements call for a rigid frame to hold the needle carriage firmly in position—but the conventional way of achieving rigidity cannot be used in the operating room.

When engineers build a structure that is not supposed to give, vibrate or move in any undesired way, they make it massive and bulky. Anvils, andirons, machine tools and many other devices are sufficiently heavy to stay put under all normal conditions. But you can't use this approach in designing a stereotaxic instrument. The instrument must be lightweight as well as rigid. It is fastened to the patient's head and will have to be moved rapidly and easily during surgery. Steel and aluminum alloys help provide a satisfactory compromise between lightness and rigidity. Yet the stereotaxic frame is by no means foolproof. The surgeon must be careful as he operates, because a slight pressure may bend it out of line by a millimeter or more.

There are other design difficulties. The slender needle is brought into position with the aid of brass adjusting knobs, the sort used to raise and lower the eyepiece of a microscope. It may miss its target entirely if gear teeth fail to mesh exactly, or if there is any detectable wobble or free play in the turning of the screws. Furthermore, the needle must be straight. If it is only a few thousandths of an inch out of line, it will be about as reliable as a a bent billiard cue. The best modern instruments for human use, which may cost more than two thousand dollars, are so designed that these and other sources of error can be controlled. The needle tip can be brought to a position in space with an accuracy of better than a millimeter.

In one sense, the instruments are far more "accurate" than nature. There was a forty-year lag between the building of the first stereotaxic instrument for animal experiments and the first use of such apparatus on patients. The main reason for the delay was that the human brain has not yet become a standardized product, and probably never will. Human brains, and the bony containers they come in, vary considerably in size and shape so that each individual presents a unique surgical problem. Considerable study was necessary before surgeons had enough knowledge and confidence to undertake stereotaxic work on man—and there is a good deal yet to learn.

Certain important steps must be taken as preliminaries to human operations. For one thing, the surgeon refers to a brain atlas, a collection of brain maps—accurate, detailed charts showing the appearance and location of nerve centers. Using such maps, he carefully plots the exact position of his "target" center on graph paper. X-ray studies are also required. As in surveying, the surgeon must have a reference-point from which distances may be measured and centers located. Since skull dimensions vary widely, however (ear-to-ear distances may differ by an inch or more), you cannot measure from the clear-cut bone contours of X-ray pictures. Drs. Spiegel and Wycis, who prepared the first stereotaxic atlas of the

human brain about two years ago, use various reference-points—
for example, the pineal gland, a flat cone-shaped body near the
thalamus at the center of the brain.

This gland, once considered the seat of the soul, may make a
suitable landmark for stereotaxic surgery. If it is calcified, which
is often the case, it shows up on X-ray films and nerve centers can
then be located with the aid of an atlas. For example, an important nerve mass in the thalamus usually lies about ten millimeters
in front of and slightly above the pineal gland. If the gland is not
calcified, other structures are made visible on X-ray pictures by
injecting air into a ventricle or fluid-filled cavity of the brain.
Such techniques have helped produce the encouraging results
reported to date.

MORE EXPERIMENTS

But some of the most extensive and ambitious trials are yet to
come. Once Drs. Spiegel and Wycis showed that stereotaxic operations could be performed successfully, other medical and surgical
investigators became interested and undertook similar studies.
Shortly after their work, specialists at the University of Illinois
School of Medicine in Chicago undertook similar surgery. Moreover, one of the Illinois group, Dr. Louis Amador, began mapping
the human brain for a new atlas. The volume, which has recently
been published, is based on more than a thousand anatomical
photographs and graphs. Special surgery has also been performed
at the State University of Iowa, the Springer Clinic in Tulsa, the
Massachusetts General Hospital, the Columbia-Presbyterian Medical
Center in New York and other American institutions. Foreign
studies are going on in France, Germany, Switzerland, Sweden and
Japan.

New stereotaxic instruments are being used to inject drugs directly into the brain, as a possible treatment for mental disorders.
Surgeons are probing deeper and deeper into the human brain.
It is now possible to get at previously inaccessible nerve structures
and treat conditions in new ways. For example, one deep-seated
nerve center—the hypothalamus—has long been known to play an

important part in the expression of emotion, and some of its cells are active when you are extremely angry or frightened. They are even more active in the brains of violent schizophrenics, and the stereotaxic needle has been used to still some of these unruly cells. That means probing about 80 millimeters or more than three inches into the brain. Surgeons speak of such depths the way jet pilots speak of new speed records, because every extra fraction of an inch represents a deeper exploration and a certain calculated risk.

Although surgery for mental illness gets most of the headlines, many other serious conditions have been treated experimentally— and will be treated more frequently in the future. There is a group of nervous diseases characterized by bizarre and uncontrollable movements of the arms, legs and body. In an effort to relieve major symptoms, surgeons have removed certain areas of the cortex, the thin sheet of cells covering the surface of the brain. But normal as well as bizarre movements may cease and the affected limb may be paralyzed. Animal experiments indicate that better results may be obtained by operating on nerve centers lying beneath the cortex, specifically on the gray cell groups known collectively as the basal ganglia.

One of these abnormal conditions is known as ballism, a term derived from the Greek word for throwing. Patients flail their arms or legs about in the wildest type of movements imaginable, and in the most severe cases death can come in two or three weeks from exhaustion and heart failure. Although the surgical treatment of such conditions is still in its early stages, some success has been reported. Operations on certain parts of the basal ganglia have brought ballism and other violent movements under partial control, without causing paralysis. In a few cases, surgeons have also been able to reduce severe tremors among elderly patients suffering from such conditions as Parkinson's disease (the ailment that afflicted the playwright Eugene O'Neill).

In the more distant future surgery aimed at the basal ganglia may aid in treating certain types of cerebral palsy. This crippling disease, which is often the result of nerve injuries suffered at birth, affects centers responsible for control of arm, leg, and vocal-cord muscles and may cause paralysis or exaggerated spasmodic movements. In certain desperate cases a radical operation has been tried with beneficial effects—removing the entire damaged half of the brain. Some specialists believe that less drastic and more effective measures will be devised using stereotaxic equipment.

Another important use for the stereotaxic approach, which has been explored by University of Illinois surgeons among others, is in the treatment of brain tumors. In about one out of four cases the mass lies too deep in the brain to be removed surgically. Previously the patients had little hope of survival; nothing could be done to slow or stop the growth process. Now they can be relieved or cured. First, X-ray pictures and other evidence are used to estimate the size and site of the tumor as accurately as possible. With this information to go on the surgeon makes a small hole in the skull, moves a hollow hypodermic-type needle over the opening and turns an adjusting knob that lowers the needle until the tip stops in the tumor (right in the center, if it is a spherical growth).

Then, with a pair of tweezers, he picks up a platinum cylinder smaller than a grain of rice—and places it in the needle. A slender rod forces the tiny object down the tube, a procedure something like that used to ram gunpowder charges down the barrels of old-time muzzle-loading rifles. This completes the operation. The cylinder contains a carefully measured amount of radon, a radioactive gas the atoms of which emit rays capable of killing abnormally multiplying cells. The so-called "radon seed" can be left in place, because its contents are so controlled that rays can do no harm to normal tissue. They do not penetrate beyond the edges of the tumor.

Stereotaxic surgery has also been called on to treat certain types of epilepsy. We have already seen that some patients, while they may not have actual convulsions, are afflicted with disturbing "psychic fits." They may feel frightened and confused, or suffer from loss-of-memory spells. Sometimes they have hallucinations of taste or smell, complaining about perfectly palatable foods or unpleasant smells that no one else can detect. Until comparatively recent times such patients were hardly ever diagnosed correctly.

They seemed to fit into no recognized medical category and were listed as neurotics, amnesia victims, and cranks or crackpots.

Investigators at the Massachusetts General Hospital have pioneered in stereotaxic studies of these disorders. Needles, inserted through a penny-sized hole in the temple, are moved slowly into the brain from the side until they have penetrated nearly an inch and a half. The target is a nerve center about the size of an olive. It is located in the most ancient part of the cortex, the "smell-brain" that evolved tens of millions of years ago and formed the original tissue out of which more advanced centers developed.

The needles may be left in place for a week or more, and are used for several purposes. Mild electrical impulses, mock nerve impulses, can be sent through them to stimulate the target nerve center. Among other things, the results help confirm that the implanted needles have been properly located (X-ray studies, of course, furnish the clinching evidence). Doctors have observed that injuries to the center may produce smell hallucinations and emotional signs of psychic fits. If the impulses have similar effects, and they often do, it is interpreted as an indication that the needles are probably in the right place.

Electrical stimulation is also being used in studies of the basic nature of human emotion. The impulses do more than produce emotional symptoms. The longer they last, the more intensely the emotions are felt. Eight seconds of impulses are enough to make the patient feel anxious. Ten seconds may bring on more anxiety and the familiar hallucinations—one patient was tested while he ate supper, and promptly declared that "this bread tastes like sandpaper!" After twelve seconds, the patient is still more frightened, begins to feel confused and may have the impression that everything happening to him is a repetition of something which happened some time in his past.

But the main goal of the surgery is to cure the patient's illness, or at least reduce the frequency of his attacks. For this purpose, doctors may send stronger currents through the needle and destroy tiny regions of nerve tissue. In some cases this step seems to have blocked some of the nerve pathways carrying signals which may lead to psychic fits. At any rate, the fits have been reduced in number and are less severe. Again, this is experimental work and it is too early to arrive at a final decision concerning the value of the treatment.

There are other applications for the stereotaxic needle. It has already helped stop unbearable pain that could be relieved in no other way. Electrical currents destroy certain deep fibers carrying messages to the brain from the spinal cord, messages which are experienced as pain sensations when they reach levels at or above the brainstem. The drug injected into the brains of schizophrenic patients at the Manteno State Hospital was administered at just the right spot with the aid of stereotaxic equipment, and similar techniques are being developed at other medical centers.

Meanwhile preliminary reports hint at a brand-new type of stereotaxic surgery, without any needle at all. Instead of a needle, there is an invisible brain probe—a narrow, extremely powerful beam of high-frequency "ultrasonic" waves. The waves have frequencies of a million vibrations per second (about twenty thousand vibrations per second represents the highest note we can hear). They are so intense that you could suffer a severe burn if you left your hand in their path for a long enough period. Even a brief exposure, a second or so, will leave your hand with a deep steady pain like that of a toothache.

Ultrasonic waves can be focused like light waves. They can destroy nerve tissue and yet do no visible damage to muscles, tendons and other parts of the body. In other words, a sufficiently intense and narrow beam would "bore" a hole only a twenty-fifth of an inch in diameter deep into the brain. Of course, you do not want a tunnel of destruction in stereotaxic surgery. You must not destroy nerve cells between the target and the surface. So the trick is to use two half-intensity beams that intersect right at the target. Neither beam alone is powerful enough to do serious damage, but they can together—and that's what happens at the point where they cross one another.

Studies along such lines are under way at the University of Chicago, the Manteno State Hospital, the Massachusetts Institute of Technology, the Burden Neurological Institute in England and other research centers. So far tests have been confined to animals. Investigators are still exploring fully the possibilities of the technique and working out technical details. But ultrasonic operations rank as one of the most promising advances in brain surgery. According to some guesses, the first trials on human beings may be made within a year or two. Whether this recent development or others come into widespread use, however, one thing is certain. The future will bring new, effective operations for sufferers from nervous and mental diseases—including patients for whom little or nothing could be done only a few years ago.

16

CHEMISTRY AND MENTAL DISEASE

Brain surgery has relieved a good deal of suffering. It has become a highly developed craft, and there is no more impressive experience than watching the precise, confident movements of a good surgeon in action. But the surgeon, for all his technical virtuosity, cannot perform miracles. As often as not, he is called in because at the present state of knowledge medicine has nothing better to offer—and this is particularly true in the case of psychosurgery. If we understood the basic causes of schizophrenia, for example, our treatments might be more sophisticated. The odds are that we would not be cutting nerve fibers or destroying cells with carefully placed needles.

A similar situation holds for many sicknesses. The treatment of most forms of cancer still stands at the stage where surgery may offer the only chance of recovery. So does the treatment of various heart diseases. A long-run hope in these and other conditions, as well as in major mental disorders, is to discover new methods and medicines—diagnostic tests to detect early symptoms, substances like penicillin and the sulfa drugs, preventive vaccines or equivalent measures. Such things call for continued and expanded research on the chemical processes whose smooth running represents good health. The brain's electrical nerve impulses are produced by high-speed chemical reactions. Every time you exert yourself, every time you lose your temper or experience an unusually intense emotion, the rate of the reactions is stepped up to keep pace with the change.

As you might expect, certain processes are unique to the brain. They correspond to the unique functions of the nervous system. A theory of the chemistry of memory has already been described, the notion that records of the past may be registered on the impressionable protein molecules in nerve cells. Whether or not this particular theory survives the attacks of skeptical investigators, one thing is clear—an entire complex of unique goings-on must be required to permit us to store vast quantities of information. Similarly, cerebral duties such as recalling events that happened decades ago and making predictions depend on mechanisms to be found in no other organ. There is obviously something special about the brain and its workings.

But this point can easily be overemphasized. Like an individual in a community, the brain has abilities and rights and privileges of its own. It is free to pursue its own interests, providing the rest of the body does not suffer as a result. The brain is by no means autonomous. It is composed of protoplasm and is subject to general biological laws, the same laws that govern the workings of less glamorous organs and tissues. Indeed, as far as chemistry is concerned, we know a great deal more about the similarities between the brain and other parts of the body than we do about the differences. So this chapter is devoted mainly to the similarities although some unique characteristics are considered.

A BUILT-IN BARRIER

The brain has many forms of special protection. As previously mentioned, it is wrapped in three membranes to help shield it against shock and injury. These membranes are clear-cut, definite structures. They can be peeled off one by one like onion skins and observed with the naked eye. But the brain is also protected by a subtler mechanism, an invisible wall which isolates it partially from the rest of the body. The first clue to the existence of this wall was reported in 1885 by Paul Ehrlich, who conducted the famous and successful search for a "magic bullet" drug to curb syphilis.

During the course of experiments to test the germ-killing powers of various substances, he noted a peculiar fact. Many dyes when injected into the bloodstream were carried throughout the body and colored most tissues with a deep vivid stain. But the brain remained uncolored. Appreciable amounts of the dyes were not invading the central headquarters of the nervous system. Ehrlich's studies have been confirmed by many later studies. The "No Admittance" policy is not absolute, however—that is, most substances are not completely excluded from the brain. Under normal circumstances they seep in so slowly that it may take hours or days before enough material has accumulated to be detected. For example, sodium injected into the veins saturates fluids bathing the body's cells in about ten minutes. But it takes more than sixty hours to penetrate the brain.

Something seems to retard the flow of many substances from the bloodstream to the brain. Investigators call it the blood-brain barrier. It is so designed that the pint of blood which circulates through the brain every minute normally gives up those substances required to keep nerve cells alive and sparking—and little else. The nature of the barrier is not certain. But investigators have conceived several models, and here is one of the most plausible. The cells of most tissues receive their nourishment by a direct route. They take into their bodies food substances that have passed through the outer walls of near-by blood vessels.

But nerve cells get their food in a roundabout manner. Between them and their meals is a vast army of middlemen, uncounted billions of astrocytes or star-shaped cells. Astrocytes exist solely to select foods for the working elements of the brain, the nerve cells that flash electrical impulses. They do this by attaching themselves to the brain's tiny blood vessels by means of long feet with suckers at the ends. A typical vessel is so densely covered with these grippers that there is little "free space," and chemical substances from the blood rarely escape directly into the fluids outside its walls. The substances first stream into the bodies of the astrocytes, which allow foods to pass on to the nerve cells and retain other materials. In other words, the blood-brain barrier is an efficient filter, a living wall whose bricks are the sucker-feet of myriads of "nurse" cells.

This elaborate structure probably plays a far more important role in nervous and mental diseases than is generally suspected. According to Dr. Robert Tschirgi of the University of Chicago, a leading authority on the problem, it may assure the proper operation of the brain. The human brain is continually on the alert to keep the individual adjusted to changes in his environment. (This is the main purpose of all brains from the human variety down.) It is a kind of automatic throttle which slows you down or drives you into action, depending on whether your needs are satisfied or not. In doing this, it co-ordinates and supervises the activities of the entire body.

The big question is how the body takes care of its supervisor. The brain is extremely fussy when it comes to dietary matters. Other organs are fussy, too, and act up as soon as there is the slightest change in their food supply or general living conditions. The brain happens to go wrong sooner and faster, as the result of even smaller changes. To provide us with a stable, dependable environment—security, in other words—it needs an extra-dependable environment of its own. "The blood-brain barrier," Dr. Tschirgi explains, "may be thought of as a mechanism for providing the brain with a milieu more constant than is possible by the blood alone."

The most intricate chemical reactions of the nervous system take place in this special environment. Although your brain makes up only about one fiftieth of your weight, it requires a quarter of all the oxygen you inhale. It contains a high proportion of fatty substances, including at least one complex compound which is found in no other organ and is confined almost exclusively to the gray matter. It contains another group of substances which exist only in nerve tissue, and are closely related to blood pigments and the green chlorophyll of plants. Also, the brain may have an exceptionally low turnover of proteins, using and reusing fragments of brokendown molecules that usually represent metabolic wastes.

The significance of such facts is not yet known, but we can say more about some simpler aspects of brain chemistry.

Your brain has a "sweet tooth," consuming large amounts of sugar. But not just any sugar, a particular kind called glucose or grape sugar. In fact, the blood-brain barrier will not accept any substitute. It screens out other sugars including one which has exactly the same chemical composition as glucose but differs in the position of a single oxygen atom. The brain is almost too particular for its own good. Since it burns glucose only, and since its sugar reserves are sufficient to last less than a minute, it is highly vulnerable to shortages. In starvation and other emergencies it receives all the glucose available in the bloodstream. The rest of the body does without, and lives on second-best substances, to insure the well-being of the brain.

Glucose furnishes the energy required for the varied activities of the nervous system. More specifically, it is a booster material, building up electrical charges in the living batteries of nerve cells. Waste energy is discarded in the form of heat, and blood leaving the brain is hotter by about one degree Fahrenheit than it was when it entered. As a rule, the brain uses oxygen to help it burn glucose as its fuel. But during convulsions oxygen may not be available in sufficient quantities for the purpose. The same problem may arise when you concentrate intensely or are upset emotionally. In such cases, glucose is broken down in a fourteen-step process which is interesting for several reasons.

For one thing, the process requires the aid of at least a dozen vital compounds known as enzymes. Enzymes are biological accelerators, substances designed to speed up reactions that would otherwise take place too slowly to support life. Place a piece of beefsteak in a solution of concentrated hydrochloric acid, and observe the meat two or three days later. You'll find that it has hardly decomposed at all. To do a thorough job you would have to boil the steak in the acid for twenty-four consecutive hours. Yet your stomach does the same thing in four hours or less, without strong acids or high temperatures—but with enzymes including the digesting substance, pepsin. The enzymes that help break down glucose in your brain have names such as hexokinase, zymohexase and enolase (the ending "ase" is a label denoting "enzyme").

To retrace our steps briefly, the blood-brain barrier is a selective sieve of a unique type. It regulates the food supply and local milieu of cells in the highest centers of the nervous system. An important food, glucose, passes through the barrier into cells where it is "dissected" by a team of enzymes to yield energy for brainwork. This chain of events charges nerve-cell batteries. It is only one of many chemical processes, which are related to one another in ways we do not understand fully. Collectively, they make it possible for the master organ of the body to carry out its special duties.

Incidentally, one further detail may be of interest as a climax to the glucose story. In a previous paragraph we pointed out that the brain during its periods of peak activity breaks down the sugar in a series of fourteen chemical steps. It so happens that these reactions also supply energy for a great many other purposes. Your muscles use them when you are doing heavy physical work. So do swimming sperm cells and yeast cells that produce alcoholic beverages by fermentation. The same basic sugar-consuming process changes malt and hops into beer (and grape juice into wine), drives the muscles of an Olympic sprinter, sends sperm wriggling toward the egg and provides fuel for brainwork. The process always has fourteen steps—and at least eleven of the fourteen are identical in all the above cases.

Abnormal Processes

Such underlying similarities among apparently dissimilar processes indicate that the brain is not a self-contained unit. Its cells may be specialized and perform unusual feats, but in the last analysis they have the same fundamental requirements as the cells of other tissues. Despite the efficiency of the blood-brain barrier, the isolation of the brain is only relative. The barrier has "leaks." Many substances get through which interfere with chemical processes and their enzyme systems and thereby upset the workings of parts of the brain. A wide variety of symptoms may result. Some substances produce comparatively simple changes; others produce weird and elaborate disturbances.

Among the drugs with highly complex effects is mescaline, an extract obtained from the flowers of the Mexican cactus known as peyote. A biologist conducting experiments on himself during World War II reported one of his mescaline dreams: "I find myself looking at the gray wall of a house. Very delicate and fragile objects resembling unshelled peanuts are regularly distributed over the whole surface, thus forming a latticelike pattern. Each husk stands on end, forming an angle of approximately 45 degrees with the surface of the wall. Violet clouds pass across the surface. This makes me wonder whether the whole phenomenon is merely a hallucination. To determine whether such is the case I close my eyes; but I still see violet clouds."

This was a dream, but the effects of mescaline usually occur when one is wide awake and last for ten hours or so. Visual hallucinations are most common, often consisting of geometrical forms and brilliant colors; various objects, one's own body and the bodies of other persons—real or imagined—may appear distorted as if they were being viewed in a trick mirror at the circus. Other effects include terrifying waking nightmares in three dimensions, and feelings of having deep and dramatic religious insights (Mexican Indians used the drug as a stimulant during sacred rites). Psychiatrists believe that these symptoms closely resemble those experienced by persons suffering from severe mental diseases.

Of course, mescaline is only one of the substances which produce psychotic symptoms. The effects of many drugs have been described in medical monographs and literary works from De Quincey's *Confessions of an English Opium Eater* to Baudelaire's *Les Paradis Artificiels*. But mescaline has a special interest today—and not only because it has been studied in recent experiments. It is believed to have been administered to Cardinal Joseph Mindszenty of Hungary, among others, as part of the Communist government's efforts to extract "confessions" of high treason and other crimes. The use of drugs to produce chemical disorders in the brain and break down personality and character is a grim reminder that brain research can be perverted as readily as any other field of scientific investigation.

Findings which could lead to cures for mental diseases may also serve the mad purposes of political fanatics.

How does mescaline work? Biologists cannot answer this question. In fact, the same thing holds for most questions about most of the drugs which produce complex and interesting mental effects. Brain chemistry has a long way to go, even compared with other aspects of brain research. But a bit more is known about certain more familiar drugs. Some of the chemicals that penetrate the blood-brain barrier easily are "sleeping pill" barbiturates, ether and the poisons cyanide and strychnine. The list also includes nitrous oxide or "laughing gas," carbon dioxide which is being used to treat neurosis, the automobile-exhaust gas carbon monoxide—and alcohol.

These substances have different effects and differ in chemical composition. But they have one significant property in common, a property they share with many other drugs. They upset the brain's oxygen supply and its use of glucose as a source of energy. Barbiturates, for example, seem to have little effect on the first and last steps of sugar-consuming processes. They interfere with the middle steps, and probably act on a specific enzyme when they put you to sleep. Alcohol offers a double threat. It can affect oxygen-glucose processes indirectly as well as directly. Chronic drinkers often eat small, poorly balanced meals. Delirium tremens and other symptoms of advanced alcoholism may be partly the result of a lack of Vitamin B_1 or thiamin. This food factor plays an important role in the chemical cycles that consume the brain's sugar.

Since the brain depends exclusively on glucose for its energy, you might expect that studies of glucose chemistry would yield clues to the causes and effects of mental illness. This is indeed the case. At the present stage of research, however, our knowledge does not add up to a clear or consistent story. It consists largely of fragments, of many new facts and observations which stimulate interest but raise more questions than they answer. For example, what is the significance of the fact that diabetes is thirty times more prevalent among the general population than it is among patients suffering from schizophrenia? Or, to put it another way, why do the patients rarely become diabetic?

Again, such questions cannot yet be answered. But other observations confirm the notion that there is some relationship between schizophrenia and upsets in the body's use of sugar. For one thing, shock-producing doses of insulin are a standard treatment for this mental disease and others. Also, the drug has been used in an effort to diagnose a certain form of schizophrenia. Administer insulin to a healthy person and his blood sugar drops sharply. On the average, it falls to half its normal level within thirty minutes. The same broad effect also occurs among schizophrenics but, according to some psychiatrists, it takes longer and the decrease is not so great. Whether or not further tests confirm this study, there is a feeling that work along such general lines is "getting warm."

The study of chemical tests for mental disease has certainly produced some fascinating and promising observations. Here is a story told to me by the director of research of one of the nation's leading private mental hospitals. Several years ago psychiatrists at the hospital released a patient who seemed to have recovered completely. Only one member of the staff objected to the move, a young chemist who had recently finished an experimental analysis of the patient's blood. His chart revealed abnormally large quantities of a substance whose presence may mean serious disturbances of sugar metabolism. He was startled, because previous tests on other cases showed that high levels of the substance are often found during or just preceding severe mental attacks. The chemist rushed to his superior, holding the chart in his hand. He summarized his findings and urged that the patient be brought back to the hospital at once. Hospital authorities, however, decided that the evidence was not strong enough to warrant such measures. Three days later the police brought the patient back. He had been picked up for throwing bricks through the windows of a department store.

In another case blood tests of a senior medical student revealed a pattern frequently found in mental patients, although the student had always behaved normally. Doctors said nothing to him—and a few months later he was receiving electroshock treatments for schizophrenia. Unfortunately, present-day tests are not sufficiently reliable for widespread use. But preliminary results indicate possible diagnostic techniques of the future.

RESEARCH ON GLANDS

Insight into the nature of mental disease has also come from a source which surprised many psychiatrists. About five years ago Drs. Phillip Hench and Edward Kendall of the Mayo Clinic first announced use of the drug cortisone in arthritis. The drug is a hormone secreted by the adrenal glands, two yellowish organs about the size of the segments of an orange and perched like three-cornered hats on top of each kidney. At an international meeting in New York doctors and reporters saw before-and-after motion pictures, in color, of patients who obtained relief from pain and swelling after injections of the gland extract.

This impressive medical show naturally inspired headlines about the treatment of arthritis. Little publicity was given to one of the interesting side effects of cortisone. The effect was mentioned in the original report of the Mayo Clinic investigators: "Several patients . . . experienced a marked sense of well-being. This euphoria apparently represented not more relief of pain but a positive factor accompanied by increased mental capacity and activity, sometimes to the point of mild 'comfortable' insomnia. Having in mind the field of mental illness, we called the attention of our psychiatric colleagues to this euphoria and they are carrying out a series of observations regarding it."

Doctors might have guessed that cortisone would bring on mental symptoms of some sort. Victims of adrenal-gland diseases often suffer from severe emotional disorders. Also, medical records show that removal of the glands was tried long ago as a treatment for mental disease. One of the earliest operations was performed in 1929 at the Charing Cross Hospital in London. During World War II a British surgeon removed an oversized left adrenal gland from a violently schizophrenic woman who first became afflicted during an air raid. The patient showed definite improvement. But the procedure and more radical adrenal surgery are not a cure for mental illness, or even a treatment for large numbers of patients. Such operations are significant, mainly because they add to the evidence an important connection between the workings of the adrenal glands and the brain. Evidence comes from the laboratory as well as the operating room. Animal experiments prove that adrenal hormones play a major role in regulating the rate at which the brain burns its glucose fuels.

Soon after the Mayo Clinic announcement, doctors throughout the country were using cortisone—and observing a wide variety of mental effects. The drug was clearly influencing the chemistry of otherwise normal brains. According to one report, one out of four arthritis patients became elated, silly and overactive. In some cases, "overactive" was putting it mildly. A New Jersey patient who had received large doses of cortisone stole three hundred dollars from a fashionable bar one night, in an unexpected outburst of energy (he didn't need the money). He was let off with a five-year probation instead of a jail sentence when his physician testified that the drug can cause "transient personality change." A small proportion of patients suffered far more severely, becoming maniacal or depressed even to the point of suicide.

Fortunately, mental reactions—severe as well as mild—can be stopped as easily as they are started. Administering smaller quantities of cortisone is usually enough to eliminate serious trouble. This fact encouraged extensive tests on mental patients, especially since the hormone definitely produces high spirits in the majority of cases. The results have not been favorable. Frequently patients feel much better at first, and the remark of a young woman suffering from schizophrenia is typical: "You know, a cloud has lifted. I have not felt like this in years." Then the effect passes and, as cortisone injections are continued, patients may become increasingly restless and frantic. When the drug is withdrawn, they relapse.

Another drug has been used in tests at many mental hospitals. This one is not manufactured by the adrenal glands, but is released into the bloodstream and circulates to them. The hormone is known as ACTH, short for Adreno-Cortico-Trophic Hormone, which simply means that it stimulates the outer layer or cortex of the glands (the adrenal organ has a cortex as well as the brain). More specifically, it acts as a kind of chemical prod so that the adrenals manufacture extra quantities of various hormones, including cortisone. ACTH is no more effective than cortisone as a treatment for mental patients. Indeed, it has similar effects—benefits at first, relapses later.

But the very fact that ACTH behaves this way brings us a step closer to an understanding of chemical factors in mental illness. In other words, it brings us a step closer to the brain. ACTH is produced by the pituitary mass, the master gland of the body whose hormones influence the activity of the thyroid, the sex glands and other organs. The pituitary gland lies encased in a bony bubble hanging at the base of the brain. Moreover, it lies near the hypothalamus at the upper part of the brainstem and, as pointed out in Chapter 3, this is one of the brain's most important nerve centers. The hypothalamus regulates vital body reactions such as blood-sugar levels, and is concerned with the expression of emotion.

The hypothalamus also controls the pituitary gland's output of ACTH. Most investigators believe that the control is exercised in a tiny part of the center located on the floor of one of the fluid-filled cavities in the brain. For example, Dr. David Hume of the Peter Bent Brigham Hospital in Boston reports animal tests which show that injuries in this crucial area inhibit, while electrical stimulation increases, secretion of ACTH. Such effects are produced by still another hormone, a hormone manufactured in the hypothalamus itself. The strange organ thus turns out to be a unique feature of the brain. Part gland and part nerve center, it is an important zone of communications where the brain and the rest of the body meet. The messages are chemical messages, carried by hormones. The meeting place is an area about the size of one of the buttons on your shirt.

A Theory about Madness

These and many research findings furnish a new picture of mental illness. Some parts of the picture are obscure, others are only sketched in. But the general outline is clear, considerably clearer than it was as recently as ten years ago. The central concept, the "trigger" that may set things off, is *stress*. Stress is a broad word intended to cover injury due to anything from a mishap in childbirth to a football head injury, infection, poisoning, old age, emotional shock of all sorts—anything which pushes us beyond our individual limits of resistance and endurance. Stress is any form of indignity which may afflict the human body.

We may be more advanced than our ancestors. We are certainly different. Stress rarely takes the form of a blow with a club or the attack of a wild animal or the fear of evil demons. But few people would deny that modern civilization offers a rich and ample variety of stresses of its own, a fact supported by mental-disease statistics. For an example of how insanity may be caused, let us take a civilized and relatively uncomplicated form of stress—say, the sheer exhaustion of a person subjected to repeated air raids. Since his cortex, the topmost center of his brain, needs sleep more than any other part, we shall assume that in this case it bears the first impact of stress.

His cortex informs lower brain centers of its fatigue. Pulses flashed along descending nerve fibers reach the hypothalamus and affect the tiny area which influences widely scattered regions of the body. Here these electrical signals are translated into chemical messages. A hormone of the patient's hypothalamus is released, flowing to the pituitary gland which secretes extra quantities of ACTH. ACTH, in turn, circulates to the adrenal glands via the bloodstream—and the output of cortisone and other hormones is stepped up to meet the emergency. These are gross and "obvious" changes which may result from severe fatigue, and which we can measure with relatively straightforward laboratory techniques. But they represent only a prelude to far more subtle changes.

Our exhausted patient is affected by a whole series of chemical disturbances, the ultimate expression of all forms of stress. As already pointed out, the way his tissues use sugar is altered by substances—poisons of a sort—that interfere with the activities of enzymes, the accelerators that keep the wheels of life spinning. We have emphasized sugar chemistry in this chapter, because the brain is unique in depending on glucose exclusively as a source of energy and because we know a good deal about glucose metabolism. But adrenal hormones also influence processes involving proteins, fats and the concentrations of potassium, sodium and other important elements in various cell-bathing fluids. Furthermore, these effects do not occur in the brain only. Changes in hormone output and tissue chemistry leave their mark throughout the body.

We can all stand a reasonable amount of fatigue. Normally, control mechanisms see to it that delicate balances are preserved. When the adrenal glands are overactive, special hormones act as brakes and slow things down sufficiently to keep the peace. When the tissues' sugar is low, extra supplies come from reserves in the liver. The very feeling of being tired can quiet us when we are headed for a breakdown. But our patient is suffering from severe and prolonged fatigue. He has no control over the air raids that keep him awake. Finally, certain control mechanisms fail, and there is nothing to compensate for or counteract unbalanced chemical processes.

Conditions are ripe for a vicious circle of self-perpetuating and self-aggravating reactions. Fatigue in the brain, the original source of stress, has produced mounting stresses in tissues throughout the body. The new stresses keep the cycle going. They react back on the already stressed brain, which sends more signals to the pituitary gland —and the entire sequence of events continues as before, only more so. The patient collapses mentally. He becomes violent, fears "electric shocks from planes flying overhead" (an actual complaint), hears voices calling him obscene names and is officially registered as a victim of schizophrenia.

This hypothetical case illustrates several points that apply to mental disease in general. Did the patient collapse because of the air raids? In a sense, yes. The fatigue and nervous strain brought on the final breakdown. But millions of other persons were subjected to the same raids, and stood up well to the same stresses. The records of World War II show that a surprisingly low proportion of a bombed population turns psychotic. The same thing holds for deeply disturbing experiences in early childhood, life in disrupted homes and any other single form of stress. As one psychiatrist puts it: "If you drop ten cups on a soft rug and one of them breaks, the odds are that something was wrong with the broken cup."

In other words, a person does not usually go mad simply because of the stresses to which life subjects him. He is already vulnerable in some way. The weak point may be located anywhere in the intricate cycle that involves cortex, hypothalamus, pituitary gland, adrenal glands—and metabolic changes reacting back on the brain to keep the vicious circle going. Somehow symptoms may be relieved by frontal lobotomy which severs part of the cortex from lower centers, or by electroshock treatments which seem to act directly on the hypothalamus and indirectly on the adrenal glands. Still, we seldom know exactly what was wrong to begin with. But we have some clues. Heredity seems to play a most important role in mental diseases of all kinds, a fact brought out by many careful studies.

Sometime ago John R., a twenty-two-year-old farmer working on his father's farm, suddenly went berserk. He refused to eat his lunch, and ran off shouting that his food was poisoned and his mother was plotting to kill him. His condition became worse, and he was finally committed to a mental hospital with a diagnosis of schizophrenia. Not long afterward, the institution admitted another patient suffering from the same disorder. The man was John's identical twin. For five years he had been working on his aunt's farm in another state. He had also run off screaming that his aunt wanted to poison him—during the same month of his brother's breakdown.

Not all cases are as dramatic as this one. But a large percentage of patients have inherited defective genes. According to one estimate, a child with one schizophrenic parent has about eighteen times more chance of becoming a victim of the disorder than a child of normal parents. (When both parents are schizophrenic, the odds are two in three that the child will be similarly afflicted.) Faulty heredity indicates faulty chemical processes in the body. One form of mental deficiency is known to be the result of a gene that prevents the tissues from using phenylpyruvic acid, a substance used in the synthesis of proteins. This "bad" gene probably works by putting one important enzyme out of action and so does the gene, or combination of genes, that predisposes certain persons to schizophrenia.

The case of the air-raid victim illustrates another significant and little-appreciated point. The whole body may be ailing in a major mental disease. Whether the cause is faulty heredity or upsets of the pituitary and adrenal glands, the effects can be widespread. Abnormal proportions of hormones in the circulating blood, for example, mean that all tissues and organs are exposed to an abnormal milieu, a "poisoned atmosphere." All cells are exposed. But nerve cells suffer most, because they are most sensitive. Furthermore, nerve cells of the newest centers in an evolutionary sense, the centers most highly developed in man, are the first to be affected by chemical changes. Cells in the highest center, the cortex, die after three to five minutes of oxygen lack. Brainstem cells are more rugged, enduring twenty to thirty minutes, while cells of the most primitive spinal centers can survive up to an hour.

This state of affairs creates a seeming paradox. Whatever we mean by "mind," it is certainly something that involves the brain. Yet many "mental" diseases are not essentially brain diseases. They are the result of disorders arising in remote parts of the body, disorders which biochemists and other investigators are learning more and more about. Considering the prevalence of nervous and mental diseases, brain research receives far too little attention and financial support. But even so, there is good reason for optimism. Contrary to popular belief, the fact that heredity plays a major role in mental disease does not imply that people are "born that way" and must inevitably suffer. Diabetes and pernicious anemia, which are also inherited, are routinely controlled by drugs—and there is good reason to expect similar treatments for many mental patients within a generation.

17

THE MOST COMPLICATED MACHINES

AN EXTRAORDINARY machine is housed in a red brick building on a dead-end lane in Princeton, New Jersey. I sat next to two mathematicians at a control desk complete with switches, dials and push buttons. The wall we were facing had a large pane of glass built into it, and behind the glass—like an item featured in the display window of a Fifth Avenue shop—was the machine. It was about eight feet long and six feet high, and the general shape reminded me of an oversized upright piano. You could look through it and into its innards, a maze of wires and vacuum tubes.

The machine was obviously running, although you couldn't see any moving parts. Hundreds of tiny neon lamps, arranged in rows across the front of the machine, formed shifting patterns as they switched on and off in a series of bright pink flashes. If you had entered the room on the other side of the glass, as I did later, you would have heard an assortment of subdued sounds. There was the hum of an electrical generator, the whir of an air-conditioning fan and the occasional rapid-fire clickings of a power switch. All this was part of the auxiliary equipment needed to run the calculating machine of the Electronic Computer Laboratory.

As yet the machine has no official name. Unofficially, it has been called a good many things. Among scientists it is known simply and rather prosaically as the IAS computer, after Princeton's Insti-

238

tute for Advanced Study of which the laboratory is a part. One evening several years ago, when it was still under construction, a graduate student jokingly offered "Maniac"—short for Mechanical and Numerical Integrator and Computer. More recently it has been referred to as "the Johnniac" in honor of Dr. John von Neumann, one of the world's great mathematicians and the man who planned it. Of these suggestions Maniac is certainly the most colorful and, taking advantage of literary license, we feel free to use that name (especially since no name has yet been approved).

Maniac operates on a twenty-four-hour schedule. In minutes or hours it regularly comes up with the solutions of equations that would take mathematicians months or years to solve. The morning of my visit it had just finished working on a problem involving the flow of water around a new type of ship hull. The mathematicians at the control desk were preparing things for the next problem on the waiting list, a study of shock-blast waves produced by explosions and jet planes attaining supersonic speeds. After luncheon— the mathematicians', not the machine's—certain design details would be computed for an atom-smashing cyclotron which may be built at Princeton University. Later in the afternoon and night there would be some experimental weather forecasting and several other odd jobs. This was a typical working day in the career of one of the newest and most versatile of the new high-speed calculating machines.

COMPUTERS IN ACTION

Such machines have encouraged another way of looking at the human brain. So far we have considered the brain as an organ, a system of nerve cells and tangled fibers interconnecting them. We have presented some facts and theories about how healthy nervous tissue grows, feels emotion, remembers, and predicts. Finally, we have outlined some research projects that promise to provide much-needed insight into one of the nation's biggest health problems, the nature of mental illness. Solving this problem calls for the continued efforts of biologists, medical investigators, physicians—all those who specialize in the study of living things. But mathematicians and engineers may yet make important contributions, and the next two chapters will indicate how.

The brain has been called "the most complex structure we know in the universe," a statement which neither astronomers nor physicists are inclined to challenge. Giant calculating machines are less remarkable but they are still worth notice, because they stand as our own creations and are the most complex of all man-made structures. The machines are made up of vacuum tubes, condensers, crystals and other devices which may be found in radio and television sets. The total number of parts may be as high as 750,000, although the average is closer to a hundred thousand.

These machines have been compared with the brain. They have even been described as thinking machines. I have made no such comparisons in this book—at least, not yet. They are based on certain striking parallels between the workings of brains and computers, and would have made little sense before the brain had been described at some length. Now we shall describe the machines, and the final chapter will discuss several interesting ways in which the brain resembles our most advanced computers. They represent a high point, a new species, in the evolution of machinery. The breed is multiplying rapidly and is certain to become increasingly prolific during the next few years.

The first of the line, an eight-year-old veteran which calculates rocket and shell trajectories at the Army Ballistics Research Laboratory in Maryland, is called "Eniac" (Electronic Numerical Integrator and Calculator). Eniac is a bit out of date today, but many new machines have names ending in "ac" as a gesture of deference to the patriarch of electronic computers—Univac, Seac, Swac, Edvac, Edsac, Illiac, even Shadrach. Others are known merely by numbers: the 1103 of Engineering Research Associates in St. Paul, and the 701 of the International Business Machines Corporation. Still others have more familiar names, like the superfast Whirlwind at the Massachusetts Institute of Technology and Oracle at the Chicago atomic-research center, the Argonne National Laboratory.

About a hundred large-scale electronic calculators are working for universities, industry and government agencies including the

Department of Defense. Less than ten years ago there were no such machines; now they have become indispensable. We need lightning-fast computers, because we have developed ways of living too complicated for our brains to cope with. The needs of society have become so complicated that we cannot keep track of and understand things without the aid of Eniac and its descendants. Take the weather-predicting activities of Maniac, as an example. We want accurate forecasts for planning picnics, raising crops, flying airplanes, sailing ships—and for planning military and naval campaigns.

To prepare those forecasts, the headquarters of the Weather Bureau in Washington, D.C., obtains a great deal of information. The information comes in from a great network of stations. About eleven thousand observers, full-time and part-time, send reports to the Bureau—facts in the form of numbers representing wind directions, velocities, pressures and so on. The numbers accumulate at an appalling rate. Every minute of every day in the year, 425 numbers are mailed, telegraphed, radioed to Federal weather specialists, an ever-rising mountain of data. There are too many facts; the brain cannot take account of them all, or even of an appreciable proportion. So the vast majority of numbers are simply stored in bulging file cases and microfilm libraries. Only a small proportion of them are used in preparing present-day forecasts.

These forecasts have been estimated to be better than 80 per cent accurate, and save Americans several billion dollars a year. But they would be still more accurate if they could be based on more weather facts. Moreover, they would be far more successful in predicting sudden shifts of weather. The weather man does well when it comes to gradually developing trends. But he always appears at his worst when he predicts snow flurries and a nasty blizzard strikes instead, or when "light showers" or "continued fair" turns out to be a deluge. Can we use Maniac to predict such events? To answer this sort of question investigators at the Electronic Computer Laboratory commonly furnish the machine with facts about the weather preceding severe storms of the past—storms that the Weather Bureau failed to predict.

The aim is to check the machine by seeing whether it can "pre dict" the past event. Recently Maniac was assigned the job of making sense out of facts available to the Bureau on November 23, 1950. After an hour it computed that a storm would start on the evening of the next day, with a sudden increase of wind velocity from thirty to one hundred miles an hour. The Bureau missed that one, which swept across the East Coast ripping roofs off houses, up rooting trees and doing millions of dollars' worth of damage. Using conventional computing methods, it would have taken six months to "predict" the storm.

Maniac does not devote full time to weather forecasts. It isn't even being used to study the future. It will continue to work on past storms, including several recent ones, so that its results can be checked against sudden weather changes which have already occurred at a known time and place. The machine is exploring new methods of increasing the accuracy of short-term forecasts—and of making precise forecasts a week or more in advance (at present such forecasts are not highly accurate). Meanwhile the Weather Bureau, the Air Force and the Navy are taking advantage of Maniac's results to prepare improved reports on a national basis

COUNTERS

This is a typical example of what the new electronic computers can do. They reduce some of the mystery of the future; they take a bit of the uncertainty out of life. Many of science's most fascinat ing accomplishments, however, depend on methods which are downright boring when you try to describe them in detail. Auto matic calculating is no exception. For all their feats and fancy exteriors, large-scale computers are simple souls at heart. Most of them are "digital" machines which means that they perform ele mentary arithmetic only. They include devices designed to perform routine calculations over and over again.

The counters, unspectacular in themselves, are one important reason why electronic computers operate at amazing speeds. For comparison, take the first counting device ever "invented," the human hand. This device was probably first used for the purpose some time around 100,000 B.C. It is still popular among children learning arithmetic—and among grownups figuring out income-tax returns or balancing budgets. Counting on your fingers may be satisfactory as an aid in solving some everyday problems, but it is too slow for more advanced computing. It takes your brain about a quarter of a second to send nerve signals to your finger and raise it into counting position.

Gears, the sort used on desk-type adding machines, are a bit faster. A gear tooth can move one position, or make one count, in a tenth of a second or so. Still faster are the relays developed after years of trial and error by telephone engineers for the automatic equipment operating at central dial-system exchanges. These switches contain electrical contacts that can open or close in about a hundredth of a second, and serve as the counting elements in some computers. But the fastest of all such devices is the vacuum tube. Gears and relays have inertia—that is, they are moving parts, and like all such parts, resist any force that counteracts what they happen to be doing already. If they are moving, they tend to keep moving; if they are at rest, they tend to stay that way.

This resistance to stopping and starting can be overcome. But it takes time, time which might be put to better use in the operation of modern computers. The radio tube also has "moving parts" of a kind. They are invisible electrons, tiny atomic particles, which can be made to travel through a vacuum at tremendous speeds. Because electrons weigh so little, their inertia is extremely low. An electron tube can be used as a switch in an electrical circuit. When the tube is "off," there is a gap in the circuit and no current. When the tube is "on" and its filament is glowing, the gap is closed and current flows. Vacuum tubes can be turned off and on in a millionth of a second or less. Each off-on operation may be used as a count.

Maniac contains ensembles of vacuum tubes counting away at a prodigious rate. But the tubes are simply doing what you do when you solve a simple problem in arithmetic. You add, carry numbers in your head, write down the answer—and a calculating machine does the same thing, at electronic speeds. Only the machines may not use the conventional decimal system. The fact that we use the ten digits, o to 9, is pure coincidence. It happens that we are born with ten fingers, so in counting by tens we are simply doing what comes naturally. But the decimal system was invented ages before the coming of electronics, and it is by no means the most natural system for Maniac and other calculating machines.

As used in the machines, tubes are "two-fingered" devices. They can be switched either on or off. They count most efficiently in the so-called binary system in which all numbers are expressed by using only two different digits, o and 1. Here is how the two-digit system works. Familiar numbers are based on ones, tens, hundreds, thousands, and other multiples of ten on. Reading from left to right, the number 2367 means two thousands, three hundreds, six tens and seven ones. Now the binary system is based on ones, twos, fours, eights, sixteens and so on. How would you translate the binary number 11011 into decimal digits? Again reading from left to right, this number means one sixteen, one eight, no fours, one two, and one one—totaling 27.

The binary system can be considered as a sort of "code" into which ordinary numbers are translated—for the benefit of machines. We might find the code a bit unwieldy, but it is a natural for computers. Imagine a row of five vacuum tubes in which the first two tubes are lit, the middle one is unlit and the last two tubes are also lit. The "on" tubes represent the digit "1"; the "off" tube means "o." This is the way binary numbers are represented in calculating machines.

The machines are setting spectacular speed records. Going back to familiar decimal numbers, how long do you think it would take you to multiply 3,696, 437, 692 by 9,731, 991, 284? It took me exactly four minutes and forty-three seconds, plus another five minutes or so to check my answer. This is a fair performance, if one has to use paper and pencil. The wiser course is to use a small gear-operated adding machine which does the job in twenty seconds and, as far as accuracy is concerned, is far more trustworthy than we are. A large-scale computer using telephone-type relays can obtain the correct answer in perhaps four seconds.

All these records have been put to shame during the past few years. The most effective electronic techniques such as those used in the Whirlwind at M.I.T. make it possible to multiply more than *ten thousand* pairs of ten-digit numbers in a single second. When it comes to speed, advances in our methods of doing arithmetic have been more spectacular than advances in our methods of getting from one place to another. A modern rocket travels only about 750 times faster than a man walks. But a vacuum-tube computer is 100,-000 times faster than the brain aided by an office adding machine. Expressed in terms of comparative computing times, this represents the difference between a few days and a millenium.

OBEYING ORDERS

Solving certain problems may call for many additions and subtractions, as well as a host of multiplications. For example, to forecast weather Maniac receives information about conditions at 360 localities in the United States and Canada. Then, on the basis of weather-theory equations, it indicates how those conditions will change at half-hour intervals. In effect, it computes how far a great air-mass travels and how long it takes, rising and falling pressures, shifting wind directions. A forecast may involve millions of arithmetic operations, all of which are performed automatically. Once a computer is started, it works strictly on its own and is expected to complete a problem without human interference.

These robots work according to principles so basic that all of us apply them without thinking whenever we have problems to solve. When you figure out your income tax, there are certain things you must know. In the first place, you need to know how much you earned last year and other facts, which should be arranged in some convenient form. Also, you need instructions which the government provides in great detail. This is the raw material for your work. Then you must perform calculations in a definite order, proceeding step by step and referring to your records at each step to refresh your memory. You'll also jot down intermediate calculations for the same purpose. After filling out the last line but one of your form, you come to your first answer—a number, the tax you must pay.

A computer must do the same things. It must include the following units: 1) an information-feeder or input device which furnishes numbers and instructions; 2) a memory organ to hold information; 3) arithmetic units like those described in the last section; 4) a master control which sees to it that step follows step in proper sequence; and 5) an output unit to communicate answers to waiting mathematicians. We shall discuss some of the devices being used for these duties. Again, Maniac provides an excellent example of the devices in action, because it has served as the model for important machines operating at laboratories throughout the nation.

Preparing a problem for Maniac can be a tedious and exasperating job. It's something like trying to explain a fine piece of poker strategy to a person whose peak accomplishment in cards is a fast game of slapjack. Theoretically, it could be done. But you'd have to explain the game of poker first, and it would hardly be worth the trouble. Maniac is a mathematical novice; it can only do arithmetic. So problems must first be broken down into "atomic" operations—exercises in adding, subtracting, multiplying, dividing. You also have to tell the machine exactly what operation to perform on what numbers, and what to do when the operation is finished.

Everything must be spelled out precisely. According to one story, Eniac is said to have blown out several hundred tubes on one occasion, because a mathematician forgot to tell it *not* to undertake the impossible task of dividing by zero. It takes weeks to translate a new problem for Maniac into such mathematical baby-talk. The complete "text" may fill seventy or more pages of written-out instructions and numbers. All the information can be registered on magnetic tapes, like those used in sound recorders. As the tapes unreel past reading devices, the machine's eyes, the information is translated into electrical pulses.

These pulses pass to special tubes where they leave memory traces. Memory of any kind depends on making appropriate marks in appropriate places. According to one theory, the brain's memory traces are stored as alterations in the shape of protein molecules, submicroscopic markings of a sort. Maniac's memory marks are glowing green spots on television-type screens. Imagine the screen of your television set crisscrossed with lines that form tiny squares like those on graph paper. A memory tube has more than one thousand such squares on its fluorescent screen, each of which may be filled or empty—that is, it may or may not contain a green spot. Forty such tubes make up the memory of Maniac.

Once its memory is crammed with information, the machine is ready to start computing. Its working conditions must be just right. For one thing, it requires an efficient air-conditioning system. You know how hot your radio set can get if its five or six tubes glow long enough. Maniac has 2,300 tubes and could turn into a furnace if the computer rooms weren't air-conditioned and kept at 70 degrees Fahrenheit. If temperatures soar much higher, Maniac is afflicted with an electronic fever and becomes delirious. The heat affects its memory tubes, producing false memories and orders which were never put into the machine. This is roughly equivalent to hearing imaginary voices. But Maniac and most high-speed computers have one virtue which is rare in us—they stop promptly when they make mistakes or receive nonsensical orders. Correct answers are printed by fast electric typewriters.

Mathematical robots are being used on an increasing variety of problems. The Los Alamos atom-bomb plant has one, a near-twin of Maniac; so does the Prudential Insurance Company (its machine has been nicknamed "Insomniac"). During the 1952 Presidential elections television audiences saw a computer predicting an Eisenhower landslide so early in the evening that commentators didn't believe it. At the request of mail-order houses a Bureau of Standards machine helped prepare thirty-nine pages of statistics showing, among other things, how women's dress measurements change with age. Machines analyze census reports, foreign and domestic business trends, public-opinion polls and a thousand other problems. Generally speaking, they are invaluable for performing long series of arithmetic operations and wading through mountains of numbers. They are "mental bulldozers" using brute speed to save the brain work.

NEW JOBS FOR NEW ROBOTS

The versatile machines are also capable of feats not ordinarily associated with computing. Their computing circuits, memory organs and the orders they respond to, give them powers of surprising scope. With the proper instructions, they can do far more than the sort of thing we usually associate with grade-school arithmetic. And the binary digits can be used to represent words, sentences and complex statements as well as numbers. Machines can thus handle many kinds of information.

For example, American Airlines has a machine in an air-conditioned room at its La Guardia Airport hangar, an electronic calculator with interesting abilities. It's called the Reservisor and does exactly what its name implies. Supposing you visit one of the airline's fifty-odd ticket offices in New York, and request two seats on next Wednesday's 10 A.M. flight to Chicago. The ticket agent will insert a destination plate into the slot of a device that looks like an adding machine. Then she will press two date and time buttons, and a button to register the number of seats requested. Within a few seconds one of three lights glows on the device: 1) a green light indicating that space is available; 2) an amber light for "no seats left"; or 3) a red light in the rare event that the system isn't working properly. If the 10 A.M. flight is filled, other morning flights are checked and possible alternatives indicated in case you want to adjust your schedule.

Your request started a familiar computer routine. It was translated into patterns of electrical pulses representing a binary-digit code for destination, date, time, number of seats. The impulses were flashed to Reservisor as instructions to look into the memory locations which contain facts about reservations for the 10 A.M. Chicago flight. This information, like the information in Maniac's memory, is stored as magnetized spots. The $500,000 automaton furnishes accurate, up-to-the-minute records of more than fifty thousand seats on a thousand flights for a ten-day period. Its memory is a kind of electronic storage bin, and it keeps a running inventory of the contents of each cubbyhole. Similar machines may be used to keep track of various items on hand in department stores, warehouses, arsenals and supply depots.

Research has been under way on even more impressive devices. The Harvard Computation Laboratory is building an automatic dictionary, an elementary sort of translating machine. Its memory will have room for a vocabulary of about five thousand Russian words and their English equivalents. All words are expressed in binary digits, letter by letter. Thus, "a-n-d" would be "00011-01100-00100." This is quite a mouthful for a simple word, but it does not bother computers which can run through thousands of words in the time you take to draw a deep breath.

The machine isn't expected to go very far in dealing with subtleties or word order and syntax, and will furnish literal, word-for-word translations of Soviet research articles. The results are not likely to win literary prizes; in fact, they can be guaranteed to make editors shudder. But scientists in the field will be able to understand what they read. Machines to help break through language barriers are being designed or developed at M.I.T., the University of London, the Battelle Memorial Institute in Cleveland and other research centers.

Other new machines are engaged in military work. Some are being tested to crack secret codes, a special kind of translating. The Army's new anti-aircraft gun, the Skysweeper, has a radar apparatus which scans space and remains glued to any enemy plane it happens to detect. The information is flashed to a computer which automatically aims and fires the gun. Computers already at an advanced stage of development can steer rockets that travel a mile or two during the reaction time of the fastest human reflexes. Before launching a missile technicians may insert into its computer a destination tape—a modern version of the rolls used on old player-pianos—containing coded charts of the path between take-off point and target. Once the missile is under way, the robot pilot measures present position (perhaps by taking bearings on stars), compares it with desired position and corrects deviations.

These are only some of the things being done by existing computers. Machines as yet unbuilt will perform many other tasks, and a frequently discussed development is the automatic factory. During the early stages of the Industrial Revolution engineers concentrated on machines which would do the work of muscles. They built weight-lifters, and subtler devices which imitated and often surpassed the abilities of fingers and hands. High points in the design of manipulating gadgets have been reached in widely different fields. One of the most intriguing machines I have ever watched had a pair of two-fingered hands—and could tie perfect pretzels at the rate of about one a second. Close relations of the pretzel-twister can be seen performing more serious duties at Oak Ridge and other atomic plants, where they move chunks of radio-active material too "hot" for human handling.

The next step is being taken. Small electronic computers are being used to operate machines that move. For example, the Ford Motor Company's engine plant in Cleveland has a computer which examines off-balance crankshafts, consults instructions in its memory organ and then "tells" a grinding machine how much metal to take off and where. Sooner or later more complex electronic computers will be hitched to lathes, milling and boring machines, overhead cranes and other industrial machinery. They will co-ordinate the activities of many mechanical slaves. Engineers no longer discuss the automatic factory in purely speculative terms. There is no reason to. They already have the basic knowledge required to construct such plants. All that is needed now is a strong enough demand and enough money—and both of these conditions might be fulfilled in case of manpower shortages during another world war.

Meanwhile investigators are working on some of the weak points in automatic computing. Eniac occupies the space of a tennis court; Maniac would fit into your living room. There is a steady drive to make smaller parts so that the same things can be done in less space, or the same space can house more elaborate machines. Each of Maniac's forty memory tubes takes up about the space of a wastepaper basket. But memory organs, ensembles of tiny magnets, are already being used in M.I.T.'s Whirlwind. They can store the information of a score of Maniac tubes in a fraction of the space. Crystals about the size of BB shots are re-placing vacuum tubes for many purposes.

One result of the trend toward compactness might be home computers no larger than television sets. They could serve as electronic calendars to keep track of dinner engagements, laundry lists, grocery bills, bank accounts and some of the other details of living. There will be hierarchies of computers, "castes" based on relative complexity. Elaborate computers will be served by auxiliary computers. Automatic devices under consideration today will help design electronic circuits for giant machines, and translate problems rapidly into computer language. The evolution of calculating machinery is in its early stages.

18

THE THINKING MACHINE

Modern calculating machines are solving problems which once required the full-time efforts of hundreds of skilled adding-machine operators. The devices help design jet planes, analyze census reports, predict elections and weather. Impressed with such accomplishments, investigators commonly refer to their creations in surprisingly personal terms, as if they were flesh-and-blood assistants. Technical reports discuss computing and memory "organs." The machines are said to "obey orders," "make judgments," "communicate with the outside world"—and, following the prevailing custom, we used the phrases freely in the preceding chapter. Scientists as well as reporters have been speaking of "thinking machines" and "electronic brains."

Just what does this sort of talk mean? And why is it sometimes resented? We tend to bristle up at the suggestion that machines do brainwork. Strangely enough, however, we would never think of arguing with a person who tells us that machines do physical work or labor. We are quite willing to accept the fact that steam shovels and other machines can do many of the things formerly done by human muscles—and do them faster and more efficiently. At the same time we take it for granted that many muscular skills from building a stone wall to assembling fine watches may never be completely mechanized.

We regard the facts dispassionately, giving due credit to the machines as well as to their designers. The same attitude could be useful in deciding whether or not machines think. But it might even be better to put the question the other way around, especially since we are more interested in brains than computers—is the brain a calculating machine? In certain ways the brain seems to work like a highly advanced "natural" computer and these similarities are worth noting, together with some important differences.

LIVING COMPUTERS

The most significant resemblance between brains and the new machines is that both can solve a wide variety of mathematical problems. Your brain is computing continually—and not just in some figurative sense. It is computing as definitely as any electronic device. Playing tennis, writing a letter, discussing politics—these and other activities are the results of long series of calculations performed by millions of nerve cells in your brain.

Like a calculating machine, your brain uses information as raw material. Information is fed into the machine by means of coded electrical impulses whose elaborate patterns represent words and numbers and instructions. Exactly the same thing happens in the nervous system. Your brain also receives raw information as electrical impulses flashed to it from your eyes, ears and other sense organs. Sensations are translated into pulses and given identifying numbers so that the brain can use them. Assigning, manipulating, classifying and comparing information is the essence of all the things we call brainwork.

Every sound you hear produces small movements of your eardrum. The membrane vibrates the way the diaphragm of a telephone mouthpiece vibrates when you speak into it. The vibrations are converted into electrical impulses, and the number of impulses is a natural code that tells your brain facts about what you happen to be listening to. Thus, an extremely soft sound may produce about ten electrical impulses per second in the nerve that brings auditory information to the brain. The loudest sounds you can hear without wincing are represented by larger numbers, creating three hundred to four hundred pulses per second in the nerve, and intermediate values stand for intermediate intensities. All sensations and all qualities of sensations—pitch, timbre, brightness, degree of pain, intensity of odor—are similarly translated into series of electrical pulses.

A relatively simple reflex illustrates how the brain may use the information fed into it. When you step from a motion-picture theater into bright sunshine, the pupils of your eyes promptly contract to pin-point dimensions. They contract to shut out excess light, reducing their diameters by just enough to keep the brightness at a suitable operating level. The very existence of such reflexes indicates that computing circuits are built into the nervous system. To adjust the diameters of your pupils, your brain requires certain information. It measures the intensity of light by counting the number of electrical impulses it receives through the optical nerve. Furthermore, it has standards of what level of illumination is desirable, and "knows" roughly how many thousandths of an inch each pupil must contract or dilate to achieve that level.

Far more subtle calculations are involved in the advanced mathematics of mind. Investigators at many laboratories in this country and abroad are devoting considerable attention to an amazing feat which we perform every moment of our waking lives. How do we identify objects whether they appear small or large, near or far away, upright, or tilted? As one specialist put it, "The fundamental thing that is happening to an organism like a man . . . going forward with his eyes facing forward, is that he is seeing the same forms in varying sizes." When you see two shapes—one small and at a great distance and turned at an angle, the other large and near-by and facing you "head on"—and recognize both as squares, your brain is executing one of its most remarkable functions.

Stated in such simple terms, the feat may not seem particularly important. But if we understood how it is accomplished, we would know a great deal about how ideas are formed and the nature of reasoning. It is a significant prototype for the deepest sort of abstract thought. In recognizing two shapes as squares, independent of their crude appearances, your brain calculates using extremely complex equations known as "invariants." This permits you to rid the forms of their apparent differences and concentrate on similarities, which is the essence of abstraction. Such processes make it possible to identify pipes, pens, cigarettes and tree trunks as cylinders—and to discover that the same laws which account for the fall of an apple also keep the planets revolving in their orbits. They are computing processes.

The brain, like a calculating machine, computes with the aid of electrical circuits. The circuits are composed of nerve cells which have been compared to vacuum tubes. Both devices may be used as relays or switches that can be "opened" or "closed" to prevent or permit the flow of currents through them. Nerve cells are the basic elements of the computing circuits in our heads. Moreover, like vacuum tubes, they are "two-fingered" devices and the brain may use them to compute in the binary rather than in the decimal system. A nerve cell is either conducting current or is inactive. It can be "off" or "on," 0 or 1, and is ideally suited to signal in terms of binary digits or "bits," as they are called. The nervous system codes sensations, computes orders to be relayed to the muscles and handles all other messages in terms of off-on impulses. The results are our actions, emotions, ideas.

Brains and computers both require methods to insure the accuracy of their calculations. One device, the Binac (binary automatic computer), does millions of multiplications an hour and contains a simple and effective error reducer. Binac consists of two seven-hundred-tube subassemblies, working in parallel; both work on the same step of the same problem at once. Each step is thus double-checked and, if the twin computers come up with different answers, Binac stops until the cause of the disagreement is remedied. The chance that the twins will make the same mistake at the same time is extremely slim.

As mentioned previously, some investigators believe that the brain may use a similar system to minimize the risk of illusion. We must be able to rely on the evidence of our senses. It is important that what we see represents a real object or event in the world around us, and the eye is designed to insure that this is what actually happens. The retina of your eye contains some 100,000,000 cells that go into action when light strikes them. But there are only about 1,000,000 nerve fibers running from the retina to the brain. An average of a hundred cells are connected to every fiber, and the response of a single one of them is not enough to make us see a speck of light. That single cell may have been stimulated accident-ally, due to some local and temporary irritation. From five to fifteen retina cells must be stimulated within a fraction of a second before the fiber transmits a signal to the brain.

Insurance against error is going on throughout the brain and nervous system. The information that pours into our sense organs is continually channeled into parallel nerve paths. It is checked so many times that our interpretations of everyday events rarely differ from reality sufficiently to do us harm. The brain is thus insured against accident and old age, as well as illusion. A vacuum tube can be removed and replaced, but not a nerve cell. Because the nervous system has its parallel paths, we can be useful citizens even with parts of our brains missing—and even though some of our nerve cells die as we grow older.

Other observations hint at how the brain may do its computing. For example, Maniac's high-speed memory consists of fluorescent green spots on the screens of television-type tubes. These spots will not glow forever. In fact, if left to themselves they fade away within a second. So they are restored to full brilliance by a scanning electron beam that sweeps across the entire screen about forty times a second, just to be on the safe side. This regular rhythm is inter-rupted only when Maniac has to "concentrate," to extract something from its memory. The scanning beam makes patterns which may be compared to those of the electrical waves or alpha rhythms of the human brain. The waves are usually prominent whenever we relax —but stop the instant we begin to take notice of our surroundings.

There are interesting similarities between the workings of some of the brain's predicting devices and the ones we construct. For example, certain computers use radar information to control the guns of anti-aircraft batteries. These computers are predictors. They aim their guns not directly at the target, but at some other spot where the target is expected to be by the time a missile reaches the proper height and explodes—and they occasionally break down in ways that remind us of certain nervous diseases. The coming of more and more ingenious computers may add considerably to what we already know about our brains.

THE HUMAN ELEMENT

But a model is not the same as the real thing. The resemblances between higher nerve centers and electronic calculators are instructive—and so are the differences. Dr. Warren McCulloch points out: "The brain is like a computing machine, but there is no computing machine like the brain." For example, the machines have puny memories. Maniac can store about fifteen average-sized book pages worth of information. The brain's capacity is billions of times greater.

If the machines had memories as large as ours, it might take them years to find any given item. We "thumb through" our memories at astounding speeds. Supposing I were to ask you suddenly, "Do you know Wilson Fleming?" The odds are that you can answer that question in a fraction of a second, although you might take a bit longer if you happen to know a person whose first name is Wilson. But think of what you are doing in that brief period. You have probably met several thousand persons, and you can add a great many more names which you read at one time or another in newspapers and other publications.

All that is stored in your head, together with vast quantities of other information. Yet without any advance notice you can explore the entire lot and come up with a yes-no answer in less time than it takes to utter the name in question. In considering this everyday accomplishment, we are left gasping. It is difficult to conceive of a device, or an ensemble of devices, that would remotely approach such speeds. Perhaps if we continue studying the brain, however, we may learn how it does the trick. In any case, comparing brains and electronic devices can give us a fuller appreciation of our own abilities.

Nature manages to perform her feats in exceedingly small spaces. Her vacuum tubes are microscopic cells; her wires are fibers many times finer than the filaments of a spider's web. Dr. McCulloch points out that the Empire State Building would not be large enough to house a computer with as many tubes as there are nerve cells in the brain—"and it would take Niagara Falls to supply the power, and Niagara River to cool it." Furthermore, the machines are out-performed by a wide margin as far as reliability of operation is concerned. Engineers are well satisfied if a computer runs several days before it develops a blown-out tube or some other defect. But the brain works much longer without making an error.

These points merely suggest what is probably the most important difference of all. Present-day machines should be compared with low-level brains only. Their behavior is a matter of "instincts," like that of insects which find food, communicate with one another and perform other elaborate actions in a relatively rigid manner. From one standpoint, however, our machines are not nearly as advanced as insects. They must be regarded as slaves. As a matter of fact, they are designed specifically to be slaves, to do only what they are told to do. If an innocent computer happens to come up with a "notion" of its own, it is promptly punished. It is turned off, overhauled and repaired.

The human element is not built into the calculating machines we have discussed. Its significance becomes particularly evident in studies of an unusual type of computer—an automatic chess-player. According to one scientist, a machine that played unbeatable chess would have to be "slightly larger than the universe." But the machine would not have to be perfect, or anywhere near it, to play a first-rate game. As part of a broad program to develop new automatic switchboard equipment, Dr. Claude Shannon of the Bell Telephone Laboratories has gone into the problem of designing such a robot. He has actually constructed a machine that ranks as a promising beginner.

Tentatively nicknamed Caissac, after Caissa the goddess of chess, it is a specialized type of computer with a "nervous system" consisting of 250 relays—about the number of cells in the brain of an ant. Caissac is wired to a chessboard, each square of which contains a button and a tiny light bulb. To start a play you press two buttons:

first the one on the square where your chessman is located, then the one on the square you select for your move. The machine flashes a warning red light if you move illegally, indicates its answering move by lighting the proper bulbs on the board, and the game is on. It plays only three-piece games in which it has an advantage of one piece, say, rook and king to opponent's king. But judging by his experience with this trial machine, Dr. Shannon is convinced that any one of the existing large-scale electronic computers could play good chess.

There are an astronomically large number of ways of playing the first ten moves alone (to be exact: 169, 519, 829, 100, 544, 000, 000, 000, 000, 000). It is obviously out of the question to examine all these possibilities. So the machine, like any human player, would discard the vast majority and employ standard openings. It would assign a definite value or number to every position it scans, and move so as to attain the position with the highest value. To do this it would draw on the experience of centuries of master chess.

Chessmen can be measured in pawn units. Generally speaking, experts consider that a queen is worth nine pawns, a rook five, and a bishop or knight three. Mobility or freedom of movement can also be estimated in pawn units. If one player has ten more possible moves than his opponent, his advantage is roughly equivalent to one pawn and the machine would include this estimate. Armed with such information, it would examine its possible moves and consider a selected few, say, four or five moves ahead. Judging by current electronic computing speeds, it could examine about two million positions in a minute. Assuming the machine was pitted against a better-than-average amateur, it would furnish stiff competition, probably winning as many games as it lost.

But the machine would lose to experts, because something is missing. The computers in use today do not act on their own, and learn by trial and error the way we often do. The British investigator, Dr. W. Ross Ashby, believes that a genuine learning machine could be built. He makes it clear, however, that the machine would require an appreciable measure of freedom: "The more minutely we design a machine to play chess just as we want it to—admitting no other information—the more certain it is to play just *our* sort of chess, with all the faults and wrongly conceived strategies. We are in exactly the same position as the father, a keen but mediocre chess-player, who wants his son to become world champion. The understanding father will not try to teach his son all chess, but will try to teach him how to profit by future experiences."

The principles which hold for chess also hold for other forms of mental accomplishment. A device built to learn the game could think along other lines, and would be far closer to a brain than the computers used today. How would it be constructed? For one thing, it would contain a very large number of similar elements such as vacuum tubes. The tubes might not all be wired according to conventional methods. A learning machine might have some permanent, soldered connections. But it would also require special connections for flexibility of response, connections that could be made and broken readily, at least during the early stages of its education.

The machine would include sensing organs, devices like photoelectric cells or microphones which are sensitive to changes in its environment. It would then be ready to detect those changes—and take account of trends that made themselves evident with the passage of time. For example, an extremely bright light would produce large effects in a photoelectric eye, stirring the machine up electrically. These effects would produce permanent changes in the machine's circuits. They would cause the machine to adjust its circuits in a particular region, so as to reduce the glare. Or, to put it another way, the machine would seek a state of least disturbance or greatest comfort.

In other words, machines can be conditioned—and not just in theory. Dr. Ashby has already built a device called the homeostat which adjust its own circuits, and is developing a far "cleverer" model. Dr. Grey Walter (we have already mentioned some of his work on brain waves) has built an ingenious electro-mechanical animal which walks about and returns to a hanger for recharging when its batteries run down. It resembles a turtle and, like living experimental animals, can be conditioned to seek rewards and avoid punishment. The device learns its relatively sophisticated behavior with the aid of six electronic tubes.

UNFINISHED BUSINESS

Such machines will have an increasingly important effect on the way we regard the world and ourselves. The brain has often been discussed as if it were basically mysterious, beyond the powers of human understanding, the product of forces and materials quite different from those which form other tissues. Advances in the technology of computers, and in biological and medical studies, indicate that the brain is no such thing. During the past generation we have learned more about the higher centers of the nervous system than our predecessors learned during the entire previous history of brain research.

On the other hand, we are clearly far from solving some of our major problems, a fact emphasized by considering the abilities and limitations of existing computers. Yet one occasionally hears it said that the brain is nothing but a machine. The assertion is usually made in a slurring tone which implies that the brain has been overrated in some unspecified way and is supposed to put an end to further discussion. One investigator calls this "nothing but-tery" thinking. It is certainly a grave insult to the brain—and to the machines. Comparing the brain to the machines of the past makes little sense. Comparing it to high-speed electronic computers can be stimulating, if we do not lose sight of the differences. But if we consider certain experimental machines, our comparisons may have more substance to them.

Our most ingenious machines are merely hints of what is to come. We can expect the gradual development of devices which are "born incomplete" and can mature. In fact, new experimental models are being designed right now. Many of the connections among their parts will be made as they age and are exposed to more and more varied situations. What would we do with the new machines? They might save engineers a great deal of trouble by taking on extra duties as they learned.

For example, you have to wait as long to complete a telephone

call to a friend you ring daily as you do to be connected with a
stranger you call for the first time. The automatic switchboards we
have today are not self-improving. They do not take account of
what connections are used often, rarely or not at all. A switchboard
which learned, however, might develop the knack of furnishing
extra-prompt service for friends or business associates. Robot pilots
might learn new methods of flying, or attacking and evading enemy
airplanes. Computers might find short cuts which would permit
them to solve problems faster.

We may have to develop special learning circuits for many of
the coming robots. If they are to become what we want them to
become and perform duties we select, some sort of preparatory
training may be called for. Such training would certainly be called
for if we wanted machines to help us solve problems so complex
that we could not even furnish precise instructions. According to
Dr. Donald Mackay of King's College in London, one of the most
imaginative physicists interested in mechanical learning: "We
should be prepared to take as much trouble in guiding the formation of a machine's 'preferences' as in bringing up a child. If we
bear that in mind, such a machine . . . could show consistent
features which in a human being we should call a personality of
its own."

We do not insult the brain by comparing it with the forerunners
of such machinery. The brain at birth can be thought of as a partly
wired device which grows and survives by completing its own
wiring on the basis of experience. Clearly, it is many orders of
magnitude more complex than the machines we have or are planning. If we still need proof, the facts concerning memory and
abstract thinking and predicting should be ample to provide it.
But the brain is enough like a machine to be investigated profitably
by the same general methods we use to investigate other physical
and chemical systems. New treatments and cures for nervous and
mental diseases depend on such an approach.

Furthermore, in coming to grips with the difference between
brains and machines we are being forced to re-examine traditional
notions about thinking—and about the human-ness of human

beings. For example, a new outlook might be obtained by considering whether or not calculating machines can be "creative" or "original." The big problem is to define in brass-tack terms just what you mean by those words. This is no academic point, because a computer can be designed to do anything you tell it to do. The only requirement is that you must make your commands sufficiently specific and clear-cut.

The commands for originality have not yet been specified. But if you defined "being original" precisely and prepared a set of highly detailed instructions for each step of the process, a machine could be built to be original within the scope of your definition. Your instructions would actually amount to a description of the machine itself, or at least of the things it would do. The machine would be original, not in the brain's way, but in the way you chose to conceive of originality. Its shortcomings would emphasize the shortcomings of your own concepts. It would help clarify your notions about thinking.

And this is one of the areas where we need fresh insights. The brain, considered as a working organ, presents science with a continuing challenge. There is something tantalizing about the fact that the most complex structure we know in the universe lies snugly packed inside our heads. It is a case of so near and yet so far. We have scaled our Everests, and there are experts who believe the conquest of space is mainly a matter of engineering and money. But we have yet to discover the mechanisms behind memory, predicting and all the other activities—named and unnamed—lumped together under the heading "mind." When this knowledge comes, and it is coming, we shall know ourselves and our universes better.

BIBLIOGRAPHY

POPULAR AND SEMITECHNICAL

Adrian, E. D., *The Physical Backbround of Perception*. Oxford University Press, 1947.

Bovet, L., *Psychiatric Aspects of Juvenile Delinquency*. World Health Organization, 1951.

Cerebral Mechanisms in Behavior, edited by Lloyd A. Jeffress. John Wiley & Sons, 1951.

Gray, George W., "The Great Ravelled Knot." *Scientific American*, October, 1948.

McCulloch, Warren S., "The Brain as a Computing Machine." *Electrical Engineering*, June, 1949.

The Physical Basis of Mind, edited by Peter Laslett. Basil Blackwell, Oxford, 1950.

Psychiatric Research. Harvard University Press, 1947.

Ramón y Cajal, Santiago, *Recollections of My Life*. American Philosophical Society, 1937.

Sherrington, Charles, *Man on His Nature*. The Macmillan Company, 1941.

Simpson, G. G., *The Meaning of Evolution*. Yale University Press, 1949.

Sperry, R. W., "Neurology and the Mind-Brain Problem." *American Scientist*, April, 1952.

Walter, W. Grey, *The Living Brain*. W. W. Norton & Company, 1953.

Wiener, Norbert, *Cybernetics*. John Wiley & Sons, 1948.

Young, J. Z., *Doubt and Certainty in Science*. Oxford University Press, 1951.

TECHNICAL

The Biology of Mental Health and Disease. Paul B. Hoeber, Inc., 1952.

Fulton, John F., *Functional Localization in the Frontal Lobes and Cerebellum*. Oxford University Press, 1949.

————, *Physiology of the Nervous System.* Oxford University Press, 1943 (Second Edition).

Herrick, C. Judson, *Introduction to Neurology.* W. B. Saunders Company, 1941 (Fifth Edition).

McLean, Paul D., "Psychosomatic Disease and the 'Visceral Brain.'" *Psychosomatic Medicine,* November-December, 1949.

The Precentral Motor Cortex, edited by Paul C. Bucy. University of Illinois Press, 1944.

Ranson, Stephen W., *The Anatomy of the Nervous System.* W. B. Saunders Company, 1954.

"Symposium on Brain and Mind." *Archives of Neurology and Psychiatry,* February, 1952.

Von Bonin, Gerhardt, *Essay on the Cerebral Cortex.* C. C. Thomas, 1950.

INDEX

Set in Linotype Baskerville
Format by Marguerite Swanton
Manufactured by The Haddon Craftsmen, Inc.
Published by HARPER & BROTHERS, *New York*